C000226592

A Certain Kind of Light

Mary O'Meara

Matador
9 Priory Business Park,
Wistow Road, Kibworth Beauchamp,
Leicestershire. LE8 0RX
Tel: 0116 279 2299
Email: books@troubador.co.uk
Web: www.troubador.co.uk/matador
Twitter: @matadorbooks

ISBN 978 1788037 198

British Library Cataloguing in Publication Data.
A catalogue record for this book is available from the British Library.

Printed and bound in the UK by TJ International, Padstow, Cornwall
Typeset in 11pt Minion Pro by Troubador Publishing Ltd, Leicester, UK

Matador is an imprint of Troubador Publishing Ltd

This book is dedicated to all my soul sisters and soul brothers. Wherever I am and wherever you are, I love you, always.

You must do the thing you think you cannot do.
Eleanor Roosevelt

One

Today I feel no pain. Not even the dull ache that frequently hovers round my head, presses down on my eyeballs and makes it hurt to look at the splendour of the sun. No pain creeping down my neck and getting knotted up in the muscles and nerve endings from the base of my skull running down my spine. Nothing pinches, nothing jars, nothing *hurts*!

I'm overjoyed. Can I really be completely fresh? Can I really be as good as new? Could I really be free at last? This is the first day of the rest of my life – without him. As I add that specific I realise it's not entirely true because he is still *there* as well as *here*. But I've come to know that he always will be. It's a bit like on one of those rare days when in full, bustling daylight you suddenly spy the moon loitering in the sky. It shouldn't really be hanging there like that for all to see – but that's the thing, it's *always* there but not normally visible in that diurnal phase, just as the sun *appears* to depart at night. Sometimes the pair will align in total opposition, sometimes in perfect sympathy. That's how it is with him and me. He's never far away and I don't need to see him to know that. Still, it's taken a long, long time for me to be able to unravel myself, to reclaim myself, to know that I am complete without him and I can walk on regardless of where he is.

'Regardless' is a very interesting word. It's not about not caring or being negligent. It simply means to do less looking. To look less at the whats, whens and ifs of *his* path – and to stop watching that pale, staring-faced clock. I can embrace my life without him playing a part in it. Yes, I can, for decent chunks of time, forget about it, forget about us. Yet, I never forget about what this means to me, what this has done to me, and if that sounds like a victimized comment it most surely isn't. Yes, it *did* do something to me, something profound. It made me stronger and braver and more loving than I ever believed I could be. A corny-sounding sound bite, admittedly, but sometimes it takes losing yourself in the chasm of someone else to really find your *self*. Like I say, it took me a long while and many false starts to reach this point – but from this point, life is suddenly limitless again. Love should never limit you and true love never will. Unconditional love is outer space and out of time, out of mind but deep, deep in the soul. I never thought I'd be standing here, looking out over the summer smog-wrapped city, declaring these things. Never thought this would happen to me. I never thought it would happen to *him*. All these things happened – or at least through my lens this is what happened, this is how it went.

Two

There was no day one.

Considering this man rocked my world to full capacity, his arrival was like a gentle summer breeze. Somehow, he arrived spiritually before showing up physically. During the August before I headed for the big smoke, I recall him floating magically through my inner world. It was the vivid blue eyes that really stood out, as was so often the case in the years that followed, but at this point of course I'd never even *seen* his eye colour, not from the back of The Kings Arms in Salford where I first saw him play the role of a Russian composer in a strange student play called *Red Square*. That was about a year before I moved to London, and though I was impressed with his performance and remember studying his profile in the drama festival programme for longer than normal at the interval, nothing felt particularly strange about this. I also recall staring at his photograph in the programme at home the next day, feeling a curious attraction. Then I put the programme away and largely forgot about it and him.

He popped up again about six months later when I happened to recognise him, playing a minor part in a low-budget film I caught at an indie film festival one weekend in Manchester. And I felt it again: a silent but unmistakable call to pay attention, like the rare occasion when a butterfly or a ladybird lands on your hand. You can't fail to notice it and feel the tickling sensation on your skin. I was struck by his good looks, those dancing cornflower-blue eyes and the oddly familiar sound of his voice.

From then on he began to occasionally float into my head. It happened a few times, maybe four or five in the space of as many months, and each time, I saw him clearly. I knew who he was but having never met him it seemed a little odd to be thinking of him like this. And I wasn't really *thinking* of him. He was just there. Just there in my head with far more presence than many people I saw on a regular basis. I had no idea why he was wafting into my mind as I went about my last few weeks in Manchester.

What I'm describing may sound like daydreaming, film-star fantasising, and I've done plenty of that in my time, but there was simply a different frequency when these images drifted in. I never consciously conjured them up; they just unfurled spontaneously and I'd suddenly be aware – *Oh, it's Charlie Gitane, that actor* – and a beautiful exuberance expanded my soul. I felt a warm, nameless happiness, as though a peculiar thrill was seeping straight out of these visions into my world, but I barely connected it with him on a personal level – rather, there was a subtle awareness that something exciting was blowing into my life and it involved the move I was making. I didn't analyse it. I didn't tell anyone about it.

When I packed my bags, my books, my records, my shoeboxes of memorabilia from my life to date, I also packed a lot of hope in my heart. A non-specific hope, a calm and childlike trust landed in my lap bouncingly,

4

late that summer. There was a journey to be made in a geographical sense. Superficially the purpose was to start my new job, and although that was definitely a good enough reason for me, I also knew it was bigger than that – far, *far* bigger than that. How different would the night sky look from a London window? What twinkling, enchanting stories could those constellations tell? At no point since childhood had I gone forward with such abandon. I was going. I had to and I was ready to shake hands with my future with a strange lack of clamminess.

Annie is a special friend of mine. We'd already shared a lot and we were about to share a lot more in the semi-sleepless city to which we were headed, and where we knew only a couple of people. I must admit it would have been a lot more daunting without her. I had a strange sense I was supposed to show her something, perhaps even teach her something if that doesn't sound too arrogant, but it was at the very least equally *me* that had so much to learn, I rapidly discovered. More to learn than I ever imagined, more to experience, more to witness, more to wrestle with than I knew was possible. Or should I say more to relearn, as at many points throughout my journey I felt I was dismantling the old ways of thinking, collapsing old paradigms, and remembering ancient, buried truths, remembering the innocence and instinct of a child, rather than the pseudo-intelligence and ego-driven progression we are programmed to aspire to as adults.

So, whether I was supposed to show Annie something or not, I'm not entirely sure, but collectively we were meant to show up. We showed up. We witnessed. We gasped. We laughed. We cried. We found it hard to leave once we arrived. It was as though we were small but vital ingredients on a certain mystical menu. Once whisked into that cosmic cauldron it would not relinquish us until the stew had been perfected. I don't know if that's fully happened yet, though the stew sure smells appetising from here. I can't speak for Annie but I know she was meant to travel with me and I'm really glad she did.

Three

We've only been in London for twenty-four hours. We're sitting in a coffee house clinging to mugs of heavenly aromatic coffee and pinching ourselves each time we remember where we are. Stockport and its red-brick homeliness seem a world away. We've traded the surly, sweeping Mersey for the inky, confessional Thames, which is flowing just around the corner from where we're huddled with our live-saving coffees. I've been too excited and entranced by everything I've seen so far to really miss it.

I sense Annie's feeling a little unsure – not homesick, but a bit scared of the huge change of scene – so I try to cheer her up with assurances that there's some grand plan at work here and that wizards and fairies and angels will make sure we are OK. I don't normally witter on about such things but the words tumble out of my mouth and drape themselves decoratively around the coffee house in a happy haze of hope.

Where were these assurances coming from? I was semi-aware that I should be apprehensive. In normal circumstances I would be, but normal circumstances had departed the minute I got on that train and I knew this without knowing why or how. On some level, when I look around the coffee shop I can sense spiritual companions smiling at us from other tables, glancing up reassuringly from their copy of *The Astral Times*. I don't know if I would have referred to them as spiritual companions right there and then and I certainly wasn't *seeing* anything literally. I would have just reported that things felt *magic!* and possibilities felt endless. *E-n-d-l-e-s-s*. And that there was *something*, something other than the fumes of the city hanging in the air, something that was keeping an eye on us, an invisible force that was keeping us company, something that was beckoning me to peep around the corner…

There's a bit of mild commotion in London right now. We discover that a small earthquake preceded our arrival by minutes and another mild one apparently occurred during our first sleep in the big smoke, though we slept through it. We joke that we're somehow responsible for this strange sequence of tremors. It feels like a fitting introduction to a new life.

Annie was reading a listings magazine. "Oh! That guy you like's in a play!" she suddenly announced.

"You mean, Charlie Gitane?" My coffee cup clattered back into its saucer with more commotion than intended. I knew full well who Annie meant but couldn't quite believe it. "Where? When?"

"Er, somewhere called The Old Red Lion – er, tonight!" Annie revealed.

Annie had been with me when I saw Charlie the first time in that play back in The King's Arms so she knew who he was. She hadn't seen the film – that film which seemed somehow to be the trigger for those funny daydream-style visitations (I use that word carefully and hesitantly, but that's how they felt) of Charlie I'd been having before coming here. For the last few weeks he had been in my consciousness more than usual and I was aware I'd been mentioning him on occasion to Annie. Bizarrely, on the train the previous day we had both observed a man with a laptop with a Gitanes cigarette sticker on it, which made me smile. We weren't actually sure why Charlie was called that, or whether it was his real name. It couldn't be. That was one of the discussions I'd had with Annie. I also didn't know for sure where he was based, though I knew from that theatre programme that he'd studied drama in London.

"Tonight?" I leaned across the table to see the listings, to see the letters that made up his unique name on the page. It wasn't just his name. There was a tiny preview of the play, which was how Annie had spotted his involvement. A wave of sheer joy grabbed hold of me. "Can we go?" I asked, knowing I had to but trying to be more normal about it than I felt.

"I'm game, yeah, let's go," Annie said.

Before we knew it, it was early evening. We'd never before been to The Old Red Lion so we set off early to locate the theatre as we didn't know our way around the Islington area where the play was happening. Strangely enough though, since we'd arrived in London, I seemed to have a keen instinct as to which was the 'right way' and we found St John Street easily. The hustle and bustle of the almost continuous rush hour around the Angel Islington felt vaguely familiar to me even though I'd never set foot in the vicinity before in my life. I wanted to buy some mints so we wandered into a mini-market, which happened to be playing *The House of the Rising Sun* by The Animals. Little did I know that this song would haunt us for the next decade and beyond, following us around like a kind of aural wallpaper, a timely backdrop that presented itself over and over in different locations and circumstances. *Superstition* by Stevie Wonder did the exact same thing. They took turns in issuing their cues but they never stayed away for long and they usually appeared during pivotal moments or meaningful conversations.

As I moved towards the checkout I suddenly clocked a beautiful, distantly familiar face and nearly jumped out of my skin. Just ahead of me in the queue was Charlie Gitane buying a packet of cigarettes. Not Gitanes, I noted curiously and with faint amusement. Annie wasn't buying anything so she was browsing the magazines a little away from me. I tried to get her attention to alert her to who was in the shop. Charlie turned from the cashier to leave and somehow dropped a set of keys on the floor, precisely at my feet. I stood back to let him pick them up, resisting the urge to get down on my knees to help him. Our eyes met for a moment as he stood up, thrusting the keys into his pocket, and the whole world slid into slow motion. He looked at me with an uncertain half-smile and I returned to him what I imagine was a similar expression, and then I tore myself away to pay for my mints while he turned to go to The Old Red Lion, I assumed.

When I'd paid I rushed to Annie, as giddy as a teenager "Did you see?"

"Yes!" she said.

"Oh my God!" I said, and I would say, "Oh my God" ad infinitum for the next decade while this man danced in and out of my life. This was the start of it and I had no idea what was coming next but I knew I was very glad I was going to see him again in a couple of hours onstage. There was a strange sense of relief about that.

For a long time that gentle relief of being physically around Charlie continued… it didn't especially matter if there was interaction or not, but I felt a recognition of being in the right place at the right time when we were under the same roof. During these first few months of our entry into each other's lives I hadn't turned it into a romance. That's quite hard to explain but it was just plain joy to learn he existed and we breathed the same air. It didn't take that long for me to notice that Charlie appeared to share that relief, at least on some level. I would see immediate uplift on his face; in his body language when contact occurred, though I was barely conscious of that reciprocation at first.

So, on that first night at the play I was simply stunned and thrilled that I'd only just arrived in London and here I was seeing this man who had been straying, strangely, into my headspace for weeks before I'd even got here, in a way no one had ever, ever done. Deep down, I had an inner knowing that he was now physically walking into my world and that those visions had been… not so much warnings, but notifications. London is a huge, sprawling metropolis and our paths might never cross again. Yet, there existed something I couldn't quite distinguish or define, something that registered halfway on a scale between hope and knowing. There was an intrinsic knowing that our paths would not just cross again but criss-cross in a magical formation. I scarcely dared believe it, but something told me, *He's here and so are you, and it's beginning.*

The Last Exit Players. Such a cool group of people. They were a bunch of actors who put on three or four productions a year. Charlie seemed to be their kind of leader, or main spokesperson, I discovered that night in The Old Red Lion. With that immediate association with impossibly cool French cigarettes that came from his odd name, he conveyed bohemian chic effortlessly and of course, that kind of style can only waft forth effortlessly. So many artistes try way too hard to be style icons. Charlie seemed to be just being himself when I observed him in the bar before the play began. The result was immediately seductive. I'd had dealings with many actors and had no time for the ego games some played. He didn't have that about him at all. The group consisted of three men, including Charlie, and two women, who I got to know in varying degrees over the years. They had that necessary chemistry to hang together well as a collective, aesthetically and socially.

When the actors had finished playing, Annie and I loitered briefly but even though I had been so excited to see Charlie onstage, in the flesh, I had a feeling of wanting to flee. An odd juxtaposition of wanting to wallow in this lovely energy that was pulsating through the venue – or at least through me, though it felt external as well as internal – and wanting to scoot. What was that all about? As time went by, I got to know this feeling all too well. We didn't stay long. We went back to our new flat in Tooting Bec and sat up drinking tea, talking about the show, about London, about dreams and laughing a hell of a lot. Always laughing, Annie and I. Giddy on life.

Four

I'm standing at the kitchen sink. It's eight in the morning and the clouds seem animated, alert, demanding my attention. I lift my eyes and see the cloud blanket suddenly pierced by a ball of yellow fire. Here is the sun! There is the sun, and a flood of excitement washes over me. It was there all the time but now I see it with my undivided attention. For a moment, I feel an absolute peace. No part of my body or mind is fighting itself or the Universe. Could I somehow live this way always? This feeling can't last, can it?

I walk to the fridge and pull out a perfectly spherical grapefruit, which I slice evenly down the middle. Again with complete, undivided attention, I cut the segments loose from the wall of the rind and marvel at the perfection of the fruit. And then the taste: sharp, astringent but so alive it somehow complements the transcendental moment I'm having. Could every moment be like this?

I'm not thinking of Charlie. Oh, he's *there* like he always is but he's not sitting in my mind, or weighing down my shoulders or pulling on my soul. Or if he is, I don't feel it right now. I feel completely happy. As I relish each spoon of grapefruit I am quietly delighted. Am I free? Is this it? Is it over? Has the new life begun? Is this how I'm *supposed* to feel? Is it a choice you can just keep making?

Five

I sensed those original 'daydreams' were some kind of premonition. They told me he was very important. He had a vital role to play – but at this point I was still wary of thinking of him as a potential lover, even though it was the obvious, human conclusion to draw. All I knew for sure was that his mere existence made me feel excited and alive.

Hudson's Cave. It sounds more like a pirate-themed pub somewhere in Cornwall than a bar in South London. I've got newspapers, a phone directory, printouts and maps scattered all over the kitchen table. London and its environs span across so much space that it's impossible to know where to start. I want to explore its underbelly as much as the surface sheen – I want to explore it all. If I'm going to make it as a performing arts journalist or whatever nebulous term describes my new job, I have to know where it's happening as well as what's happening and I don't know where to start... only that I keep getting nudged towards this cafe bar called Hudson's Cave. Having scanned countless columns of listings and marking an X besides obvious places that have a reputation and interesting bills, my eyes keep being drawn back to Hudson's Cave. When I look up where it's located I'm surprised to discover that it's actually just down the road somewhere, probably no more than ten or fifteen minutes' walk from our flat. It isn't included in many of the major listings. According to its stripped-down but cryptic website, some radical playwrights' group perform impromptu performances there on occasion, and it's also a music bar with a popular club night for new bands on the first Thursday of the month.

A week after our arrival in the capital city, Annie and I stumbled upon Hudson's Cave accidently. We'd been spending most of our time in other areas of this giant urban playground, including Camden, Brixton and Shoreditch, and hadn't really explored much beyond our own doorstep. I had it on my agenda to check out Hudson's Cave but hadn't got round to it as yet, but as we turned a corner by Balham Tube station we both got a fluttery feeling that something was happening round here, and it was at that moment that we spied Hudson's Cave, nestled in a terrace of shops and restaurants with its creaky sign blowing pensively back and forth in the autumn wind. We also both felt some trepidation about entering the venue. What if it was a secret society? What if you had to know the secret knock or handshake to be admitted?

I started feeling so panicked that I suggested we pop into a nearby pub for a quick drink before exploring the Cave. Annie agreed, as for some reason she had the jitters too, and we soon found ourselves semi-involved in a pub quiz that was happening in The Bedford, a fairly normal pub a few minutes from the Cave. I had a strange feeling of blending in and being 'at home' in the general area. Balham felt oddly familiar, though neither of us had ever set foot in it in our lives. Elements of the quiz tickled us, though I can't remember the jokes now, and we left after a whisky and Coke with a feel-good giggly feeling.

Hudson's Cave was about five minutes' walk round the corner but suddenly it seemed as though we'd been directly teleported to outside its entrance, as though our feet hadn't touched the pavement or crossed any roads. Hmm – something, some kind of energy was swirling and propelling us along. It made no logical sense.

Inside the Cave it was noticeably darker than your average interior, but that appealed to me. The floor was wooden, scratched and well trodden by garrulous drinkers. Creativity lived and laughed within these four walls. I could tell that straight away and I was happy. We ordered another whisky and Coke and it seemed that no, there were no membership criteria, or if there were we had been admitted. I wondered if Hudson was a living person, and then I clocked a man with a tattoo of a grey-type alien adorning his bicep prowling about, snatching empty glasses from tables. I knew instinctively that he was Hudson.

A guy with a record bag arrived and bounced up to Hudson, who shook his hand. Hudson gestured to him to get himself set up in the DJ booth. While he was setting up, Hudson took to the stage a couple of times to scatter various witticisms around the venue. He had the knack of swift delivery and over the years as I got to know him, though he was occasionally cruel, he was for the most part strangely nurturing and generous with the performers. The performers came in all shapes and styles, from singer-songwriters with acoustic guitars to stand-up comedians, zany poets, dancers, drama groups and even the occasional full rock and roll band. That first night Annie and I were in the Cave was purely a DJ night. I was enjoying the Northern Soul records the guy in the booth was playing and the general vibe was warm and upbeat. People came and went consistently through the creaky door. The evening was obviously popular, with a constant medium-level hum of activity. I got the impression that people were drawn here for a reason they couldn't quite explain, just like I had been, though I wasn't especially wondering why I was here.

Except suddenly I knew.

My eyes were drawn to the foot of the stairs that led up to a small upstairs gallery and out onto the roof. To my astonishment and delight there was Charlie Gitane yet again! I say astonishment, yet it was more astonishment that he had come so quickly rather than that he had appeared, because on some deep level, I wasn't completely surprised that he had manifested once more. And he did manifest in a most peculiar way – almost like his energy was assembling itself there in a whirl before my eyes; a sort of cosmic calibration was occurring and when it had settled down, I saw him standing there as though finally fully formed.

I quickly realised he wasn't alone. He was accompanied by a strikingly attractive woman with silky chestnut hair cascading down to her mid-back. I wasn't sure how I felt about that. This was his girlfriend, I assumed. Should this bother me? Did this bother me? At this point I can say no – because at this point I hadn't seriously entertained the thought that he and I would ever even get to know each other. I was simply stunned at his arrival again, and equally stunned at his beauty. Seeing him offstage and off-duty, I actually felt even more attracted to him. There was a certain kind of light that seemed to hover around his being. He reminded me of someone or something dear, ancient and soulful, something so familiar yet so shockingly new that all my senses were in overdrive, marvelling at the reappearance of this man in a big city like London in the space of a week. What the hell was going on here?

I subtly alerted Annie. It was hard not to stare. Bit by bit, as time went on I realised I wasn't the only one staring. Bit by bit, over weeks and months I became aware that he had a tendency to stare at me in an equally entranced manner. I still just couldn't quite believe he was staring at *me*, not someone behind me or a painting on a wall. Yet it became clear that he was. He was here again, less than a week after the night at The Old Red Lion.

For the rest of the evening I alternated between staring and averting my eyes, and Charlie appeared to be watching too, but only in passing, and I wondered if he recognised me from in the corner shop before the play a few nights back. For some reason it didn't even occur to me to go and speak to him, to say hello, to tell him I liked the play the other night. It was almost as though I knew there would be plenty of opportunity for that, as though, right now, I could only handle short episodes of being in contact with this extraordinary energy. The energy wasn't exactly emanating from Charlie – or that was my impression. It was just in the air, and even when I was at home for the next few days the excited buzz would suddenly bounce off me again, and around the room. Even at this stage, I knew my life would never be the same again. And I was glad.

Six

Today it feels expansive, so wide, so high, so all-encompassing, it's all about us, and it's all not about us at all. It's so, *so* big. I stretch out my arms and I just can't contain it all. And that's part of the beauty of it. It won't sit in a box or allow a lid to hammer it down. It can slip into a padded cell in the dead of night. It can unscramble any combination on any safe or break through the mightiest fortress. This connection started it, opened a door, a very wide door that leads into a vast and magical land... it was the touchpaper, it lit the flame, it *is* the flame – but the light is everywhere and can reach anywhere. Today I feel nourished by the bond, by the link, by the inexplicable shared flame. Let it blossom, let it burn, it can never, ever go out. It's that light I heard about, yearned for, recognised when I saw it.

The dreams started charging the nights with a strange, enchanted energy that was hard to ignore. I've always been a vivid dreamer and always credited my dreams with being something more than random images to entertain, scare or puzzle me. I'd already had a few prophetic dreams in my life and even though I hadn't figured the details out, I simply knew I went places and saw things that weren't 'just dreams'. It was clear I was an avid astral traveller but didn't consciously think that was what I was doing, and nor did I even intend to do it. It just happened – it had happened all my life but it happened with greater frequency and intensity since the arrival of Charlie.

The room at the back of the flat in Tooting Bec where I slept had some cheap plastic blinds that didn't darken it a great deal. I remember many nights of waking from sleep, as though being summoned by the moon to bear witness. The moon always seemed to be a sickly yellow colour during this time, and it regularly climbed to a spot outside my window and blasted the room with insistent, restless moonlight. I had many grand, narrative dreams in that room, as well as many snatched, incoherent fragments that oozed all over the duvet and evaporated rapidly by dawn. Lots of the dreams involved Charlie, and those ones tended to be characterised by particularly high definition, sharpened focus and extra-vibrant colour. It was as though someone suddenly tore a hole in the fabric of the space and time that separated us and I could see him in a completely real, multidimensional way. Sometimes I didn't even have to be asleep for this to happen, though I'd normally be in some sort of quiet, reflective state for that veil to be lifted. His eyes were always especially blue, and the camera of my mind would normally zoom in on his face, which could be wearing any expression. This happened very early on and just carried on happening, perhaps once every month or sometimes a little less than that. I'd never be willing it. It was always at least a faint shock and even now, ten years later, it can still amaze me with its clarity and realness.

But the dreams… they could be charming and magical, filling me with happy awe – or darkly disturbing, capable of unsettling me for the rest of the day. Sometimes they involved some harm coming to Charlie. The details weren't always clear, and these dreams were often cloaked in a historical mist. Around this time I had a strong feeling that Charlie had been hung on a gallows in another life – or at least it was planned that he would. Some part of me felt he was saved at the last minute. Where this idea came from is hard to pinpoint other than through a sequence of dreams, waking images and information that I just seemed to already know, as though I was recalling it rather than learning it for the first time. Not only did I see images of those gallows, but I also knew that the site of them wasn't far away from the dingy Tooting Bec flat we lived in for our first six months in London. One day I dreamt the gallows were on a peculiar mound positioned in front of the flat, just across the way. I saw them in my mind's eye all too easily. I knew I'd been there. I'd witnessed the build up to the horrific scene, but couldn't quite ascertain if he'd died. I also had a sneaking suspicion that I too had come to a sorry end in a similar fashion – though I suspected mine had involved a burning stake. Of course I never told him any of this and I had no idea if there was any truth in it. They were just spontaneous impressions that rose to the surface of my consciousness at this point in time. I knew how crazy it would all sound to anyone so Annie was the only person I confided in.

I also 'knew' he'd been a highwayman and we'd had some shocking affair – in fact, a sense of shock or outrage was imprinted on many of these fleeing 'memories' I labelled as 'past life memories' simply because I didn't know how else to define them or explain them. Prior to this, I had neither accepted nor rejected the idea of reincarnation. I was open-minded. Still, I'd never pulled from past lives like I seemed to be doing since arriving in London. It was like I was walking onto the set of a period drama and all the characters who had been poised in long-term sleep had been reawakened. It may be more accurate to describe this as only a partial awakening. They were only fragments of scenes and sounds that triggered the suspicion that this was some sort of reassembly or continuation of an old story. My awareness was bright at times but dim and confused at others, and sometimes I only half-believed what my soul was telling me. I didn't want to believe it, and I didn't at any point try to conjure any of this up. Many of the characters struggled with their lines or sense of purpose, like they couldn't remember what they had to do or why they were being reactivated. But they all showed up. We all showed up. We were all there and perhaps there was some kind of karmic choice involved as to what we did.

I started my job on Monday. I was the performing arts editor at listings, entertainment and community issues magazine *South of the River*. It was a dream job for me, having been a scribbler and theatre obsessive ever since childhood. I'd had a flirtation with being an actor myself during my student days but I felt after a while that I was somehow being assigned the role of commentator, reviewer and interpreter – even nurturer of the artists I encountered, rather than a fellow performer. It was a welcome change from struggling to get freelance pieces in the press, which I'd been doing for several years preceding this lucky break back in Manchester. I liked the magazine's ethos, which was experimental, aimed at the independent, alternative and sussed South London dweller. The lines were a little blurred at the magazine, and I helped out with work outside my field here and there, but that didn't bother me. Maybe this was because my sense of reality had become blurred. Since meeting Charlie nothing was ever quite what it seemed – or what seemed impossible was possible. Likewise, what seemed logical was often turned on its head. Previous presumptions were continuously up for review. Preconceptions were shaken and stirred with the ice rattling and clinking around in the glass, making music of an unusual kind. Music I'd never consciously heard before – yet it was wonderfully familiar, and struck a sequence of chords that I couldn't explain or ignore.

I loved my job straight away and stepped with a strange ease into the role as though I'd been doing it for years. I don't know why. I usually find new jobs very daunting and think of walking out and not coming back by lunchtime on the first day. But it was as though the magazine had been awaiting me and I got to know the ropes with an odd sense of déjà vu popping up left, right and centre.

It was on my third day at work that it happened. I was pinning a poster for a new playwrights' group on the corkwood noticeboard at the foot of a flight of stairs, outside the cafe which was affiliated with the magazine. The hub of offices the magazine staff worked in were positioned at the top of these stairs. The noticeboard hung within a small indoor courtyard with a non-functioning, paint-spattered fountain, just off Balham High Road. As I stood pressing drawing pins into the board, I felt a pair of distinctive eyes boring through my back. It was an intense gaze, and the kind I normally associated with being eyed up in an 'I fancy you' type of manner, yet it was much more than that too. It was 'I recognise you' just as much. I struggled with getting the final pin into the tough board and the energy felt strong enough to topple me over, so I cautiously turned around.

Charlie. Who else? Even then, it was 'who else?' when I hardly *knew* the guy. I mean, we'd never even spoken… yet. He was pulling on a cigarette with a cup of coffee in his hand. He gave me a smile that was an endearing mixture of playful naughtiness and apology. We stood for a moment as though in a trance, then both moved towards each other slightly.

"Do you work here?" he asked needlessly, as it was obvious that I did.

"Yes," I replied as he scanned the playwright poster with apparent curiosity.

"That sounds interesting," he remarked.

"Yes, it's a new group I want to set up to hopefully get some local writers involved with some new plays," I told him, hardly believing this was happening. What was he *doing* here? I guess there could have been many reasons.

"I'm Charlie," he said, holding out his hand.

Without a thought, I found two words had fallen out of my mouth. "I know," I said, and immediately wanted to kick myself as we shook hands. "You're one of the Last Exit Players."

"Yeah." He looked somehow embarrassed about that fact.

"I'm Eileen," I told him.

My boss suddenly appeared and wanted a word, so I was whisked away.

I didn't see Charlie again for about three weeks, which was probably just as well as it was as though I'd been chucked into a rapid spin cycle in the 'processing strange spiritual phenomena' machine. I remember at school learning how many of the Romantic poets 'suffered' from hyperaesthesia. I'd grasped intellectually what this meant, but now I knew. And it wasn't just my five senses that seemed to be in overdrive. My sixth sense leapt into gear with a strength it never had before. Not that it had been dormant, as I'd always been in touch with the unseen and uncanny and never dismissive of those things, but it was the way it pervaded the everyday that was startlingly different. I suddenly just *knew* things, random things or bigger things, it didn't discriminate, and what was especially noticeable was that the sixth sense proved itself to be correct repeatedly, and usually very quickly. I gasped at the intuitive notifications that kept being flagged before my eyes. What was going on? What lid had been lifted? It was exciting though slightly exhausting, but I was young and healthy and I didn't want it to stop.

For a period of around a year or more I don't think a day went by without some wonder or weirdness in it. I'm not complaining about that at all. In many ways it was like some kind of return to childhood. I'd never completely lost that wonder, that belief in fairies, and that the world was far more exciting than the drab veneer that had been draped over its magical truths by a rigid, finger-wagging society. Although Annie and I joked about all this, I can honestly say I was not dismissing all the strange happenings that had been going on ever since we'd set foot in London. There was too much to dismiss, and also it appealed to me way too much. Life was meant to be this exciting. This was actually how it should be. More and more it seemed that I'd mention that something might happen and that very thing happened in minutes. I sensed invisible helpers, and potentially hinderers, hanging out in the trees and bushes and dropping stardust in my hair. Some might say I needed some psychiatric assessment, but I knew I hadn't lost the plot. I was delighted that all this did exist after all.

Naturally I told Annie about my encounter with Charlie in the courtyard of the *South of the River* offices. I told her many of the things that were happening but I didn't quite reveal how deep this was hitting me, how I felt I'd been swept away, like a boat from its moorings – and that this wasn't exactly normal. Yet, we did speak of that too. Annie recognised the enchanted energy and though she was a level-headed, sane person, there was something about Annie that was quite childlike. She adored children and had an innate understanding of how to connect with them, so I think she had a respect for the strangeness. Over time she began to witness encounters between Charlie and myself, and she agreed that something extraordinary was going on, but as I've already reiterated, it was always bigger than just the Charlie factor. It had long, swirling arms that seemed capable of throwing sparks all over the world. Annie and I started to go to Hudson's Cave on a regular basis and more often than not, walking home we would experience unexplainable things. We heard wind chimes when there was no wind. We'd see black cats cross our path at a rate that was way above the law of averages. Over the next few years, the law of averages ceased to exist. Foxes too seemed to manifest and emit mysterious, ethereal energy on pivotal street corners and in car parks, preceding or following significant events.

"I can't believe I said, 'I know' when he said who he was." I cringed slightly, remembering the moment. On the surface it seemed an almost rude response. Annie just laughed. We both did. The utterance of "I know" was completely involuntary. I suppose it was my soul who, I've come to believe, had known this other soul, currently embodied as this person named Charlie, for many, many lifetimes. The question was, or one of the questions was, did *he*, Charlie Gitane, know who I was? Not that my name was Eileen McCarthy and I was thirty-five years old, from Manchester but with Irish origins, recently moved here to work with the magazine. No – did he have the same sense of deep knowing that went beyond superficial biographical details that I did? Or was it just me? All along I suspected it was mutual but I wrestled with myself about this for a long time, instead of trusting what was being clearly shown. It's much easier in hindsight, and I now think to myself, *How did I miss that? How did I doubt that?*, but when you're waist-deep in cosmic soup it can get cloudy and messy. And when it rains, the deluge feels like some biblical catastrophe. But the beautiful thing was, I had never felt so alive, so animated, eager and excited to embrace each day. Would I see him? When would I see him?

What about the others in the group? I got to know all of them, bit by bit, as well as some other characters connected with Charlie. People linked to him seemed to pop up all over the place and randomly spouted information about him or asked me about him, as though I was some kind of authority on this man, who I still hadn't known very long and there was no real reason why people should associate us much of the time. But these were some of the things I got used to. Unexplainable phenomena became almost unremarkable, though never fully unremarkable because I still pinched myself regularly and discussed with understanding friends (and there weren't many) whether any of this was normal. It took a long, long time for me to be OK with the fact that it wasn't normal and never would be, and that the abnormality was actually a good thing, a chance to revolutionise my consciousness. I struggled with trying to make sense of the irrational and mysterious, instead of just accepting that this was a journey where signposts and maps could shape-shift and endings and beginnings could reverse and recede and return – and return.

Seven

There was a day – it was in June, but it felt like November. Charlie had been away shooting a low-budget film in Wales for around six weeks. I'd stepped out of the offices to post some letters at the quaint little corner post office run by a smiling family who handled each item with such care it was a joy to go there compared with the anonymous experiences city-dwellers are accustomed to. I walked each step with an odd sense of anticipation that appeared to have no cause until I saw Charlie appear a little down the street, close to Balham Tube station. I should have known he must be back when I'd felt that quivery feeling, that scentless but undeniable aroma that permeated the air when he was near. I didn't know exactly where Charlie lived at this point, just that it was clearly somewhere in the same general area as me.

It was so cold for early summer that he was wearing a long, dark coat that looked oddly familiar to me and gave him the air of a Russian soldier. I could feel my stomach flutter, my heartbeat stepping up. He was on my path so it was inevitable we would come face to face, but the decision of whether or not to speak was somehow bypassed, and this became a feature of my interactions with him. It was as though when we were in the same space, a certain kind of energy took over and I'd find things had come out of my mouth without censorship.

We spoke for a few minutes, mostly about the freezing, unseasonal weather, but I remember this day because of the magic in his eyes, the magic in the air, the magnitude of the reality that he had become a character in my everyday landscape – this beautiful man who shot straight to my head, like a glass of good wine on an empty stomach, was really walking the same streets as me. I felt ridiculously happy just to see his face, and to stand and have a casual conversation on the corner with him seemed a thrill. Even though it was misting, not snowing, I could feel little atoms, like ethereal flakes of snow, dancing around our faces in the beginning of June. I walked on to the post office, smiling inside and outside. I didn't analyse this especially. I didn't even wonder if he felt it too because on some level I knew he did, but I hadn't consciously gone down that avenue yet. It was enough to take on board that he was actually here. The dream train had dropped us off at a platform in the real world. Was it a mistake? Would one of us get swept off again? How long did I have in this state of altered reality? What the hell was happening to me? And was it happening to him too?

I don't know if I'm moving too fast or too slow with telling this story. It can't travel chronologically because even though there are dates daubed on discarded calendars, dates smudged in defunct diaries, dates etched in various brains and wastepaper bins, this was not a linear process so it can't be a linear story. Even now, a decade down the line, I'm aware of the overlapping cycles and stages; even now, even though things have stabilised to some degree I have learnt that I can't predict the future and nor do I want to – though by all means I can travel there and backwards too, even if I can't decipher the departure and arrival boards!

So, Charlie had a girlfriend who I heard was a dancer currently working in a West End production. Her name was Elaina and I viewed her as impossibly beautiful and cool. I even strangely approved of such a chic and attractive woman to complement such a handsome dude as Charlie. It made perfect sense. With any other man I would have thought along the lines of not being able to 'compete' with the likes of Elaina. But here was another exception to the rule. The word 'compete' didn't figure. I had no intention of competing and I knew it wasn't about that on a deep, deep level, yet my rational mind declared I shouldn't have a chance in hell. *But I knew I did.*

I knew I was supposed to have a chance.

When I first got to know Charlie I don't think I fully believed he could be interested in me as a girlfriend, but I knew very early on that he was interested *in something* about me. It was the way he looked and watched and spoke. It was also the electric energy that surged through the paving stones when we met on the street, that set the air on fire when we'd bump into each other in Hudson's Cave or Cafe Noir, a bar not far from the magazine offices and close to the new flat in Ramsden Road which Annie and I moved into around this time. There are such things as one-sided attractions and I've been on both ends so I know the unfortunate, uneven feeling of those, but there was no way in the world these energy exchanges with Charlie were one-sided. Together we made a highly charged cosmic circuit. There was a magnetic pull that surpassed anything I'd experienced to date. I knew he felt it too, but for some reason I didn't fully accept this. It seemed too good to be true. And I thought, *If he does feel drawn to me it's for some other reason than my looks or personality or whatever the chief ingredient in normal attraction is. It's because I remind him of someone.* His mother, his sister, a previous lover? I had no idea, but unmistakeable recognition lit up between us each time we came close, like two long-separated magnets that somehow got thrown back into the same space. It wasn't something I could really explain, but it was as though our meeting was triggering some distant, almost unconscious memory in both of us, something I strained to elucidate and could only ever glimpse.

Now, perhaps all these years later I know... we were simply remembering who we were, who we are – meeting each other somehow activated our true selves.

There was no doubt that an unusual energy seemed to have swooped upon me ever since I arrived down south, and that this energy seemed to gather intensity when Charlie was around. I could feel the air almost crackle at times. Could there be a straightforward reason for all this? Or was this a whole series of coincidences that were just piling up all over the place for the sheer hell of it? I tended to conclude that there must be a reason but it didn't seem to be a straightforward one. Charlie had been in my life for almost two years now, though there'd been absences throughout that time – mainly when he went on tour with the Last Exit Players, or was just elsewhere, or I was just elsewhere, but there was rarely more than a couple of weeks between some encounter or another.

Some encounters stick out prominently for me,

though each and every time in his presence was never taken for granted, was never humdrum, was never without emotion. I don't know when exactly I fell in love. It was there from the start but I didn't dare admit it, and it didn't feel like any other love I'd ever known. Indeed, so many of the problems attached to our relationship may have arisen from trying to squash it into the normal parameters of a regular romantic relationship. To try and make sense of both our behaviours – the endless questioning about what was happening and why didn't do me any good, but as a human being it made sense to try and make sense of things, though I would have been as well to just accept it as the unique situation it was. I didn't have the tools to do that, and nor did he. He didn't give much away on one hand. On the other, he showered me with a type of energy that was impossible to ignore, and the more he tried to hide it or disguise it or make it seem casual, the more it seemed to slip out – and there were days when it seemed to leak all over the floor in big patterns of joy and desire.

Bit by bit, we just seemed to end up hanging out in the same places: Hudson's Cave or Cafe Noir, or at plays and gigs or on the street. I bumped into Charlie all over the place and it did cross my mind that he *must* be wondering the same thing as me on some level – *Why is this happening? Why is he/she everywhere I go?* – but it wasn't just the frequency of unplanned meetings, it was the feeling that accompanied them, the knowing even before the physical recognition, like the rumble of a distant train alerting me to the fact that –bang! – *Oh my God! There's Charlie.* Then there was something about the way he often appeared visually – like he was bathed in a certain kind of light, like a misty sunrise, like a mirage, like a dream … come true. Sometimes it all happened in slow motion; other times it went in the blink of an eye, but always with a feeling that left me glowing, excited but oh, so nervous. We both were. We both tried to hide it.

Eight

When did it start going wrong? Or was it going right all along? Going to a universal plan, not my plan? It all seemed to be a matter of perception... of acceptance, of surrender.

I wish I'd learned to surrender earlier but sometimes you can't surrender until you've been through that hell – until you're down on your knees imploring the Universe to take over because you don't understand, your brain is fried and your soul is literally sobbing.

If I'd only realised sooner that I couldn't control the situation it might not have been so hard, yet controlling myself was really where my lesson lay. I was never so dumb to think I could control him and had a disinclination to even want to do that, even if I could. Yet, I had a strange feeling that if I worked at it in the right way, if I did everything in my power to help make this happen it *would* happen, because why on earth would we have been brought together like this only for nothing to happen?

Not that *nothing* happened – so much happened – but the fairy tale romance element, though wafting in the air with undeniable presence, though alluring and seductive and always *there*, was not necessarily what all this was about.

I can't remember when I had that realisation but

I had hints of it for a long time before being able to say there might be another reason, or multiple reasons. *Yes, he's clearly the man of my dreams – literally – but does that mean we are destined to be together? What the hell is destiny anyway?*

It was the month of August and we'd had a spell of hot, bothered, pre-thunderous weather. I'd been covering an event called *London Calling* – billed as three nights of the best new drama that was being showcased at various small venues around the city in the hopes of attracting sponsorship from larger theatre companies and funding bodies. In truth there wasn't a great deal of chequebook-waving or uncorking champagne. The reality for most actors was playing in all kinds of dark corners with malfunctioning sound and lighting systems and sparse audiences for the majority of events, though here and there players and playwrights did break overground and go on to dizzier heights.

The three nights in Hudson's Cave that year were positively buzzing and I had a litany of eager thespians to cast my senses over. Tonight was the last night, and an after-show party of sorts was happening in the bar. It happened to be Charlie's birthday and he and his entourage tumbled into the full-to-capacity bar just as Hudson decided to bolt up the doors to stop anyone else squeezing in. I knew many of the entourage at this point, though none very well, but that night they all seemed to know me and I observed winks and grins and comments that I couldn't figure out without resorting to the notion that he had been talking about me – or somebody had. Elaina was there too and seemed a little sullen – but that didn't stop her being beautiful and I could appreciate how Charlie must be smitten with her. I asked myself how he could really be interested in me when he had this goddess at his side, but even as I asked the question I knew something was wrong with my whole take on it. I knew he was interested but I didn't know how or why, and perhaps neither did he. That night, Charlie and Elaina were standing right against me in the clammy bar and I felt uncomfortable. They weren't speaking and there was a hint of fury in her aura and a kind of shoulder-shrugging, 'swallow another drink, worry about it later' energy to him. I tried to move away but I felt glued to an invisible strand that seemed to link us, no matter where I squeezed myself in the crowd. There was nothing tangible you could see with the naked eye but I couldn't get away from the feeling of unseen threads being spun around our bodies. I don't know how aware of me Charlie was that night, but his friends sure were. What was going on? That night I ached to be with him, not necessarily in a romantic sense but just in some kind of solidarity or understanding, but I knew I couldn't be. I also knew all was not harmonious between him and Elaina. Was I secretly glad about that? Well, quite honestly, no. I wished them well and sincerely thought they looked great together. But I did get the impression she wanted something he couldn't give – or vice versa. I felt bad for even wondering if they would split – but I did start to wonder this.

Following that same *London Calling* event I was conducting a couple of brief interviews with some of the actors and writers that caught my attention during the festival. It was Sunday afternoon and a smattering of various creative endeavours were manifesting around Hudson's bar again.

I was admiring some artwork for a new production that one of the playwrights was showing me when Charlie came in, a little uncertainly. He seemed to come for no real reason. No one he knew seemed to be there other than me. I shared the artwork with him and he agreed it was awesome. He seemed to want to talk but at the same time I got a sense that words weren't the medium he needed, as though he knew they were inadequate for what he wanted to convey. I turned my attention back to a playwright I'd been talking to and got on with things but it was hard not to watch him out of the corner of my eye as he floated about, unable to anchor himself. I didn't have the nerve or arrogance to think he'd dropped in specifically to see me, but at the same time I knew that was at least a part of it. After twenty minutes of drifting around, he came to say goodbye, and tapped me on the shoulder in a way I was growing to love, as he often did this. It was a subtle, distinctive communication that bypassed any superficial chatter and went straight to the heart, to the soul – we were finding ways to reach out to each other but neither of us really knew how or what we were attempting to reach. Whatever it was, it was already there. It was within our reach. We were lucky enough to have it in constant supply but neither of us knew how to navigate these unchartered waters, these strange natural highs that existed simply through breathing the same air together. It was too good to be true. Too true to be doubted, but doubt it we surely did.

It was again a Sunday morning, about a week later.

I'd dropped into Hudson's Cave to collect something and discuss some business with Hudson himself. I was barely inside the door when Charlie turned up, clearly hung-over and sleep-deprived. He told us how he'd almost got run over on the way to the bar and was a little shaken to have had such a near miss. I quietly gave my thanks to divine intervention or good luck – or whatever it was that had avoided a tragedy that morning. Charlie was very much alive even though he really did look like he'd had a close scrape with the other side. He moaned about feeling awful. Hudson paid little obvious attention, but I knew he was watching us in the curious way people tended to.

Charlie had a childlike habit of climbing on furniture, and today he decided to lie flat on the sofa at the head of which I was perched, wondering if I was still supposed to be there. He lay himself down like it was the obvious thing to do and I found myself looking down at his ashen face with wonder and tenderness. Hudson was still flapping around and muttering about the cash and carry. I realised I could very easily plant a kiss on Charlie's forehead or cheek. I could easily reach down and stroke back his hair. In fact, it seemed the obvious thing to do. I resisted.

I made some kind of small talk with him which I can't recall, but I clearly remember him looking me right in the eye and saying sadly, "There's a hole in my soul", which I knew there was... at this point it wasn't a big hole and it was certainly capable of healing. I wanted to heal him, take his pain away. I wanted to love him. I did love him. It was undeniable. What were we doing sitting in a closed bar on a Sunday morning in a position like this? Why were we so often in strange, unconventional positions?

Hudson had things to do and Charlie seemed incapable of moving. I'd done what I came to do originally and I felt I'd better go before I did or said something I might regret. Hudson ordered me to lock them in. I can't remember why. I locked them in and went home, pondering. This man was so important to me. *Does he know how I feel? Do I know how he feels? Am I supposed to 'save' him? What does that mean? Why is he telling me he has a hole in his soul? Did I do the right thing? What's it all about?* I did way too much pondering. I still do, but much, much less. A lesson I needed to learn had definitely started.

Nine

It was around this time that I had a chat with my friend Laura about psychics. I'd had tarot cards read for me a few times in my life and always had a fascination with the world of psychic phenomena, ghosts and the unexplained, but it wasn't until the situation with Charlie happened that the quest to know and understand what was happening became more pronounced; that I began to actually explore rather than wonder if any of this stuff was real. My experience is that we undoubtedly do have a sixth sense and it can be as helpful and wonderful as any of the others. I would learn, slowly and fearfully at times, to examine all kinds of other possibilities, to challenge what the media and government present as facts even more than I already did – and I'd always been the questioning type. I realised, with joy, that there truly was much more to life than meets the physical eye.

I found myself confiding in Laura about my feelings for Charlie following a night we spent in a hotel back in Manchester. We'd been delegates at a *Guardian* newspaper journalism event during the day. That evening she told me about some odd paranormal things she'd witnessed, which led me to share a few of my own. Laura had recently got a job with a holistic health magazine where metaphysical talk was the order of the day and not something to be hushed up or treated with the suspicion it often can be in the normal world. Through a friend at the magazine Laura had recently come across an American/ Turkish lady named Zharha, who was the best psychic "in the world!" according to Laura. The minute details that Zharha had observed about Laura's life, with no prior knowledge or conversation, had knocked her to the floor.

"Actually, I've got her card." She rummaged in her handbag as we sat on high stools in the Malmaison hotel bar. "You should call her, Eileen. She'll tell you what's going on with this Charlie guy."

I stared at the small card Laura had passed me, seeing a photo of a very beautiful woman. She had an exotic air about her, and I could sense some kind of extraordinary power or wisdom pulsating from her just from the photo.

"Thanks, Laura," I muttered, carefully putting the card away inside a pocket in my purse. "Maybe it would be a good idea."

"Trust me, it would be," Laura said, refilling our glasses with what was left in the wine bottle. "She doesn't talk any bullshit. She can be pretty blunt but that's what so good about her. She won't feed you any fairy tales or bollocks."

I had probably known Charlie for just over two years at this point. That was certainly long enough to know that this felt fated, powerful, transformative, scintillatingly beautiful – throwing me down a well of wonder that I hardly imagined could be so deep or nourishing… or perplexing.

I lay in my hotel room that night, playing back much of what had happened with Charlie to date and wondering if a psychic consultation would be a good idea. Wouldn't it be good to get confirmation that I wasn't imagining it, confirmation that he felt it too? Or what if she told me this was all in my head and I needed a reality check? *Nah! It is real*, I argued to myself. I had a growing sense of needing to discuss the invisible, to make sense of the enormous feeling of delightful expansiveness that pervaded my life since his arrival. I struggled to define the bond – or experience. I didn't even know what to call it. 'Relationship' felt like the wrong choice of word and 'friendship' didn't seem to quite work either. I mean, we did know each other reasonably well at this stage but I was aware I'd had these feelings from the start, before there'd been any chance to get to know him. How could that be? I knew something special and rare existed between us, but having said that, I did question whether it was going anywhere. Would we become something other than the fairly casual friends most people would probably have viewed us as at this point? Even in asking that question, I knew there was nothing casual about any of it, nothing accidental, nothing irrelevant, no matter how it might seem looking at it in an everyday, superficial context. I guess at the end of the day I could sense I was becoming enmeshed in a journey unlike any I'd embarked on before. I'd met the love of my life but I barely dared believe it was happening. It could just be a dream, couldn't it?

Even though I worked with choosing words and descriptors every day I somehow lacked the vocabulary to explain what I felt about Charlie and what was happening here. It didn't work that way. It wasn't an intellectual or scientific or even psychological concept. The message the Universe was trying to give me was that *life* isn't a concept or a series of concepts, a series of habits, knee-jerk reactions, prejudices or automatic conclusions – but I wasn't getting it. Along with many others on this planet, I lived far too much in my head. But logic and brainpower were failing me here. Despite my near-incessant questioning there weren't any answers, but at this point I still thought I could somehow figure it all out.

This experience was forcing me to *e-x-p-e-r-i-e-n-c-e*. There was no point in avoiding it but I didn't want to just free-fall into that giant crater that had appeared on my path, at least not without a parachute. Everything in my psyche was being challenged in order to clear out the junk, the self-limiting stories, the stuff that held me back from being who I truly was and from being truly alive – but I couldn't step out of my own way enough to view it as a passport to freedom rather than some kind of endurance test that might have a prize at the end in the shape of Charlie. Yet, I knew that meeting him was a spiritual springboard – propelling me off the cliff of conformity, exiling me from my comfort zone, whether I liked it or not. I hung back but stepped forward at the same time, and strangely enough, I felt Charlie was doing a similar thing, peering over the edge and marvelling at what was just out of reach. We were both dipping our toes into a new way of being – or that's how I saw it – but both pulling them back out when that fear came crashing down, which it surely did, again and again.

As time went on, though, my feelings for him grew to the point where there was just no denying I was both hopefully and hopelessly in love. Something extraordinary was evolving, but at the same time stabs of anguish began to creep into the situation. I wanted to be with him. I wanted to tell him. I wanted to find out if he felt the same.

I arrived back in London at lunchtime the next day with Zharha's card tucked in my purse. It somehow soothed me. Little did I know back then she was to become my mentor and dear friend. One of the positives of the Charlie story was coming to know her. I have no doubt she was sent by some celestial being to help me through the rocky years that lay ahead. She changed my life. It would have changed anyway, I know, but she was a catalyst, a healer and more than anything a companion. She helped me mop up the mess I sometimes found myself in but she didn't just stick Elastoplast on me – she showed me those wounds, we examined them together and she led me to stare right into the big, gaping holes in my being; holes that we all have in some form or other. The ones we hide. The ones we try to fill by any means we can. She dared me to think bigger and to walk and talk my path. Yes, I might have ended up walking it anyway, as the Charlie experience stamped my soul's passport with indelible stamps that said, *AWAKEN* and *HEAL* and *LOVE*, but without Zharha, I would have had a much harder time. Much harder.

One January night I had a memorable encounter with Charlie in Hudson's Cave. I was down there for a quick drink having just finished some editing and thought I would check out the Cave and see if anything interesting was going down. I was alone. That was the funny thing: since meeting Charlie I'd become far less fearful of entering a bar on my own, or of being on my own in general. It was as though somehow, the experience was forcing me to face myself and that meant being fully embodied in my own presence, daring to stand alone and trust I had enough light of my own to keep burning. Oh, I loved good company and still do, but I've learned to love my own as well. That took a long time, as all these things have.

Annie was holed up in the flat working on an essay for the Masters in creative education she was doing, but I didn't have any close deadlines and fancied popping out – so I did.

I was glad when I entered the Cave and saw Charlie. He looked equally glad to see me. He had a friend with him that night, nicknamed Mackie. I'd seen Mackie before but didn't know anything about him. That night for some reason I trusted the vibe Charlie was giving off – the one that said, *Approach me!* – so I did, feeling a little nervous and hoping I wasn't being cheeky by joining him and Mackie. Charlie was clearly pleased and kind of encircled me to prevent me sneaking away again. I can't remember what we talked about. It wasn't important but I was happy just being around him, as I always was.

I believe it was that night that I finally asked him if Gitane was really his surname. He said, "Not on my birth certificate", but it had become his name ever since he attended the East 15 Acting School where he had earned that name from his "bad habit" of smoking French cigarettes and generally being "a bit of a Francophile". He shrugged and grinned at me. "There's no more myth to it than that, unfortunately."

I hadn't seen him for around a month before that

January night and had been hoping for a chance encounter almost every day since Christmas. At one point, Charlie got called away by Hudson and I was left with Mackie, who seemed strangely shy. I asked him if he was an actor too. He laughed and almost apologised as he said no, he was a plumber. I reminded him how important that was. Charlie was back in a flash. I don't know if he thought Mackie and I were getting too cosy but he barged in between us, holding a copy of a free music and listings magazine that was often found in bars in those days.

Charlie held the magazine and turned the pages as though he was inviting us both to read it with him. He made comments and jokes about some of the rock-and-roll characters that inhabited its pages. I realised from the things he said that we shared a very similar taste in and opinion about the current music scene. The thing that struck me most, though, was his hands, which, while holding the magazine, were quietly shaking. Why? I knew why. Some might say perhaps he was withdrawing from a drug, or that it was some physiological reaction to a medication or whatever – but I knew very well what it was. It was that same shaking feeling I got around him some of the time. The one I disguised as best I could. It was both the joy and terror of getting close.

That night I realised he felt it as much as I did. My hands weren't shaking but then I wasn't holding up a copy of the magazine, and besides, the energy wasn't reverberating *all* the time or we'd surely never even dare speak to each other. What, oh what was this thing? Yes, it's normal to feel nervous when you are strongly attracted to someone but this always felt like so much more than that.

It was palpably something in the air. It was like some third energy that was generated when we were both in the same physical space. The same energy that I also could feel at a distance at times that alerted me when he was coming or was close. It was undeniable. Sometimes it could literally make me shake. Sometimes it merely resulted in needing to run to the toilet. Sometimes it made me want to run away, and occasionally I did bolt. That night I realised that he seemed to have the same response. It wasn't just that I could *see* the shaking. It was that I just *knew*.

Of course, I never mentioned it. I remember once joking to Annie that Charlie sometimes treated me as though I was liable to give him an electric shock. At the time, that annoyed me a little as I sometimes felt him shying away from touching me, as though I might be radioactive. At other times he touched me fearfully. At others he touched me compulsively – or so gently, so lovingly that I could melt. When I say touch, I mean on the back, on the arm, a kiss on the cheek. Nothing more intimate than any of those things, but those things were certainly intimate with him because everything was. We were joined in some way – it was spiritual but had strange ramifications in the physical. Ramifications that my body and probably his too were struggling to digest or take on board. That was on a pure physical level before bringing in the emotional whoosh and wash that had been pushing and pulling for some time now. That night I *knew* he felt it too.

Even though I was very sure of this I didn't know what to do with it. I felt I couldn't blurt something out; perhaps he would. Or should I? But what about Elaina?

Even though she seemed not to be around these days I didn't know for a fact she was gone, and quite possibly she wasn't. By my own code of ethics, I couldn't make any kind of move on a man while he was still taken. And besides, I'd so much rather it came from him... in the traditional way, even though I also knew the traditional rules were not applicable, were null and void, obsolete and nothing to do with this unusual relationship we found ourselves in.

It was hard to sit with it when I got home. It was late and I made a mug of tea and logged on to the computer and scanned my emails as though looking for an answer there. Annie had gone to bed so I was alone. A thought popped into my head. Should I call that psychic? Could that really help?

That night I just wanted someone to help, but who? Some straining part of me just asked the room. I asked the ceiling and the carpet. I was pulled to Zharha and it felt somehow inevitable I'd make that call. From out of my purse, stashed amongst other cards for restaurants and businesses I found her card and noted she had a website address printed on it. Excitedly I turned back to the computer and typed her name into Google. A mystical, shimmering page appeared and I read curiously through reviews from people around the globe, all testifying as to how astoundingly accurate she was. Looking closely at her photo again I saw warmth but absolute honesty in her eyes. I got a sense that she was like some Middle Eastern prophetess of old, someone that angels spoke to, someone that kings and queens would have consulted in ancient times. People had written that she *doesn't beat about the bush* and *tells it like it is.* I needed someone to give it to me straight. I needed the truth. I needed help. OK. I took a deep breath and clicked on her email link. I was worried about what she would tell me but I also had a deep sense of knowing that she was going to be the voice of sanity here. That she had a message I needed to hear – even if it wasn't the one I wanted.

I awoke in the morning from vague and rapidly departing dreams, unable to remember anything of substance from them. I had a meeting with a local promoter about a mini festival he was running in Morden over the May bank holiday weekend so I had to leave the house fairly early with some scribbled questions on the back of an envelope. I just had time to check my email before I left, and my heart jumped with anticipation when I spotted a reply from Zharha. On opening the email, I saw it wasn't from Zharha personally but from her assistant, Jasmine, asking me to phone to arrange a time for my consultation. OK, this was it. I was going to learn the truth and hopefully get some answers.

It was two days later that I found myself walking down the King's Road in Chelsea, fighting an icy wind that made my eyes tear up, heading for the address that Jasmine had given me. Despite my nervousness I was very keen to meet and speak with this amazing-sounding woman. I expected Jasmine to answer the door and lead me to a turret at the top of the building where the mighty Zharha would be seated, draped in chiffon with the scent of beautiful incense wafting from her very fingertips, but to my surprise it was Zharha herself that answered the door, and told me to "Come on in. Eileen, right?" in a completely down-to-earth, laid-back fashion. I followed her inside and down the hallway where she gestured to an office. There was no chiffon or incense, no Buddhas or angels, but there was a lovely sofa in front of me covered with colourful silk cushions, which she invited me to sit on. The aroma of freshly ground coffee was permeating the office from the kitchen nearby and somewhere in the building I could hear what sounded like a couple of small dogs yapping.

Zharha offered me coffee and we both sat down with our cups on the sofa and I stared at the painting of a mountainous landscape she had on the wall.

"So, Eileen, what brings you here today?" Zharha asked me. "No, don't tell me!" She immediately put her hand up to stop the words about to topple out of my mouth. "You want to ask me about him, this man."

"Er, yes," I confirmed, knowing she didn't need to be psychic to deduce that. I expected that most women who visited wanted to ask about a guy, but still I was slightly alarmed that she seemed to already have him in mind. I just knew she *did* have *him* in mind, him specifically.

"OK," Zharha said slowly, and shut her eyes for thirty seconds or so. "He has a name that sounds a lot like…" Then she opened her eyes. "Ch-Ch…" She was searching, and I was gobsmacked already. "Charlie?" she questioned.

"Charlie," I said plainly.

"That's him, yes." She grinned. "OK, and what do you want to know about Charlie? Does this guy smoke a lot?" she added with a cough, waving her hand in front of her face as though waving away cigarette fumes.

"Er, yes, quite a bit," I confirmed, not then realising that she might be picking up on his peculiar surname.

I stated that we were friends but it felt like there was much more. I told her I wanted to know what he felt and what might happen. I wasn't sure how else to phrase my questions, which felt bigger than that. They sounded so pathetic when spoken out loud to Zharha. They sounded silly and clichéd, even though I knew they weren't.

I remember her first words being, "Well, I already read this as a romance. At the moment, I get him slightly turned away from you. This is him trying to figure out if he wants to make this something more. He's like a guy perched on a cliff deciding whether or not to jump. He's full of fear. If he does, you will be there to help him fly."

I listened and marvelled. Yes, that was precisely how it felt. She proceeded to tell me that we would become a couple but it could take a long time. She had told me what I needed to hear. I wasn't imagining this. Yes, he was interested, but yes, he was terrified and yes, this needed to be given some time. Somehow speaking with Zharha settled me. I instinctively trusted her. I felt she could totally see us, and our positions. I left her house in Chelsea very much at peace.

Ten

I had a dream around the spring of 2004, which I still remember with a slight shiver. Elaina appeared in my dream looking tight-lipped and resigned. She was carrying a black rose, which she wanted to give to me.

She said, "You can have him. I've finished."

I didn't tell anyone. I didn't want to be the recipient of these slightly eerie premonition-type dreams, though I later learned I had no choice. I knew what the dream meant but I didn't trust or distrust it, until one evening, as shadows began to fall, I went to the kitchen to place a mug in the washing-up bowl. I stopped in shock to see a woman was standing near a car parked on the street outside our rented flat in Ramsden Road. It was Elaina. She looked upset and a little crazy. She looked up at my window and fixed me with a look that made my blood run cold. It was a look that suggested she was angry with me. I felt a sense of panic. Why would she look at me this way? Or was she just looking this way in general and it wasn't directed at me? Had I just happened to be in her line of vision? She couldn't know my feelings, could she? As far as I knew, Charlie had never acted strangely towards me in front of her, other than one time I recalled where he did seem a bit over-friendly, but she'd only looked on with mild curiosity.

I came away from the window and stood back in the rapidly darkening kitchen. Somehow I knew I'd never see her again, and I didn't. I felt a wave of odd energy surge over me that seemed to come from outside, like a karmic echo. It was one of those things I couldn't explain or understand. I just *felt* it and it scared me a little. Whatever had gone down between her and Charlie I didn't know, but I could sense it was heavy and that even if he was suddenly free he would definitely need space and I'd better be careful here.

I wondered later if I was too careful.

I'm a dignified kind of person generally speaking, and normally highly sensitive. I didn't want to tread on Charlie's toes and if he was finished with Elaina I assumed that would soon become clear. As it happened, it didn't become clear for a while and during that time Charlie and I danced around each other delicately. Neither of us seemed to want to take a risk. For me, this was mainly because I wasn't convinced it was over with Elaina. I felt they had separated, yes, but I felt there was still contact and more than likely, still feelings. It may sound strange but I couldn't figure out who left whom. I sensed that he was hurting. Because I sensed this, I held back. I knew from my own experiences and general human nature that people need time to grieve. Because I cared about him deeply I didn't want to step on an already aching heart and complicate things. I wanted him to come to me in his own time if indeed this was what he wanted, and though most everything told me it was, only he could make that clear to me. So I continued to hope and pray he would.

I spoke to Zharha again about a month later and she said much the same things. She also told me not to cling on too tight.

"Holding on too tightly may mean the bar of soap slips out of your hand," I remember her telling me. I didn't fully understand what she meant as I hadn't lived through the holding-on-too-tight experience for long enough just yet. I knew I was holding on to hope and the dream that I had allowed to take root. It had grown quite strong and healthy roots already. I watered the dream with love. I carefully eradicated any weeds that tried to get tangled up with it. I was starting to watch the kettle boil, too intently perhaps, which meant it took forever to do so, but I scarcely realised I was doing this.

Having realised in my mid-thirties that I had finally found the man of my dreams, I wasn't going to let him slip away. Still, what was I to do? *Just let it happen* seemed to be the answer I generally got when I shut my eyes and asked. Despite its undeniable intensity, this was never an obsessive kind of love. It was tender and true. It was soft and gentle. It was big and bright. It was east and west smiling lovingly at each other. Extraordinary though it was, it also felt completely natural, as though it aligned perfectly with the architecture of the Universe. It felt preordained. I had this instinctive feeling that this was a gift that had been bestowed on me. That I was duty-bound to nourish it and look after it, to see to it that it blossomed.

I'd never had something so seemingly perfect arrive on my path like this, and yes, you could easily argue that I didn't *have* him in the most obvious sense, but I knew I had experienced something precious just by having him arrive the way he did. This thing was alive and part of me. It was in my heart. It warmed me and kept me going. Even on dark and dank days the thought of Charlie shone a certain kind of light on the landscape. I couldn't let this fail. So, I lived the next few months having some lovely, encouraging times in his company, punctuated by the occasional bout of worry that someone else would step up and claim him, or that Elaina would return and I'd feel like a fool.

Jason, usually referred to as Jay, was a scenic designer and sometimes a film-maker. He and Charlie were close buddies and were very often together. Many a time when I bumped into Charlie on the street, Jay would be with him, though there were equally many times when it was just Charlie. It was always nice to see Jay too. I felt some kind of soulful solidarity with him and we always managed to find something to laugh about. I felt at ease with Jay from the start and was very fond of him. I would even go so far as to say I felt I already knew him on first meeting, just like Charlie, though it was somehow more mellow, more relaxed, not as shocking to the system as encounters with Charlie tended to be.

I remember late one afternoon in the early part of rush hour, I was walking on one side of Balham High Road whilst Charlie and Jay were on the other, probably having left the studio the Last Exit Players were renting at that time. Charlie was waving wildly at me, determined that I would notice him, and though I did eventually I must have been seriously steeped in the cavern of my inner world as they were adjacent to me before I clocked them. I waved back and then walked on, with a mildly giddy feeling that almost always accompanied even a glimpse of him. Something made me look back over my shoulder that day and I remember seeing the pair walking on, with Charlie appearing to be gushing to Jay about something or other. Jay's demeanour was calm and steady whereas Charlie's tended to be more mercurial. There were times when I thought to myself, *Jay must notice how over-the-top Charlie's waving is, how at times he seems to almost jump out of his body when he sees me.* He wasn't subtle, but equally I don't think he was really aware of how energetically our encounters seemed to switch him on, just as they switched me on. I concluded that Jay *must* be aware of this. When I looked back at Charlie jabbering to Jay and Jay listening, I felt the conversation was to do with me. What was he saying? *Does everyone know except me? Or could I have this all wrong?*

I still didn't really know what to think about it all, but as encounter after encounter followed similar patterns it was impossible to believe this attraction wasn't mutual. But it wasn't just an attraction. It was bigger than that. There's that phrase again. I'd always known this.

It – whatever it was – flooded our immediate environment and I knew others felt it too, though I didn't know on what level or how conscious they were of what was triggering it, or even what exactly *was* triggering it. I saw it as some kind of new but simultaneously ancient energy that was immediately activated or even alchemised by our meeting. It was like a call had been issued to a cast of characters, that the torch had been set alight and history was about to happen – or re-happen. Charlie and I were not the stars of the show because there were no stars. Ego had nothing to do with this. I had a lot to learn about ego and how I would end up stripping it away, layer by layer.

That stripping away of ego was a big and necessary part of this journey. I never realised what tremendous suffering ego caused until many years into this 'relationship', but I knew I was being remoulded very early on. It was akin to a huge restoration work on a long-standing, no-longer-fit-for-purpose building. Superficial patching and painting wouldn't do here. After some initial surveying and exploration it was clear that this building, this soul, was going to be gutted, flattened, demolished and rebuilt, stone by stone by stone. The end result would be worth it, as the blueprint I sometimes glimpsed was stunning. Still, the path to this new shape was not an easy one. It required demolishing all those structures made of fear, the ones that limited and constrained and were built on false foundations. Only then could love really grow – and without walls or roofs or conventional canopies of any kind, it could both shelter and nourish the world.

During the time that Elaina ceased to be visibly with Charlie a certain kind of fear began to lodge itself in my soul. It was as though I felt I had this window, a limited time span in which to get it together with him – but I wasn't clear if the window was really open or why I felt such a sense of urgency. Also, I know now that my idea of what 'getting together' meant was flawed because I was thinking along traditional lines, when this was not a conventional connection. One of us had to ask the other out and then we'd become an item and then live happily ever after, right? Although that was what I wanted in one sense, because it's all I ever knew as a normal progression of boy meets girl, some part of me knew this wasn't how to navigate the ship with the slippery deck I was trying to balance on, but I had no other tools with which to proceed. I had this feeling that if I didn't *act* in some way I'd lose the chance, but how to act? There was absolutely no acting, no pretending, no option other than being my true self. Yet, I seemed to distrust the notion that it would just happen, even though that was what my inner voice was telling me. Looking back now it wasn't about taking action at all, but about *being*. Yes, I had a lot to learn.

A wake-up call arrived one Saturday night in May. Annie and I went to Hudson's Cave for a few drinks. As soon as we arrived I was stunned to see Charlie sitting at one of the small, circular wooden tables with a woman I'd never seen before. She was blonde, slender and had a slightly timid air about her. They looked like they were maybe on a first date – or could they be old friends? A rush of anxiety overtook me but I had to hold it in check as I was in a public place and I didn't want anyone to notice that this had knocked the wind out of my sails. Thank God for Annie, who was a supportive presence and had some inkling of what I was going through. She knew how I felt about him and she had no doubt that he felt something major too. Annie was one of the few people in my life who never doubted this thing; never told me I was crazy or to get a grip. I'll always, always be grateful for that, and more so because I knew she was an honest soul who would have warned me if she thought I had lost the plot.

I'd always tried to keep a dignified front in public but that night it was hard. *Charlie.* He'd had a few drinks and possibly some other chemicals. He seemed to be avoiding me. Normally his eyes followed me round the room just as mine followed him. Just being in the same place as him tended to be intoxicating for me. I don't know what it did to him but for me, it sustained me for a short while, a quick fix like a sugar hit from a chocolate bar, until I'd start longing to see him again. Each exchange was a little precious piece of heaven, which I'd lie in bed and replay, feeling it wash over me like a gentle breeze. Tonight was different. In my mind he was behaving badly. Was he ignoring me on purpose? Or was he genuinely wrapped up in this woman's company? It didn't *look* that way. They didn't seem hugely into each other. She seemed quite subdued, perhaps nervous. He seemed like he was going through the motions – neither happy nor unhappy. My hunch was he just wanted someone to talk to, someone to give him some attention, and maybe someone to sleep with that night.

Much as I disliked seeing what I saw, I didn't want to leave because some part of me wanted to find out what was going on, and I ached for him to notice me. I wanted him to come over and explain that this wasn't how it looked, knowing full well that wasn't going to happen. I don't know how long I stood there witnessing this sorry scene, but for every minute I stood there I felt like I was being slowly beaten up. Was I masochistic? I don't know. I was hurting and I truly couldn't understand how he could do this to me. Yes, I know we weren't together – arguably we weren't even close to being together from the perspective of most of the world. Yet I knew in my soul that we *belonged* together, and no matter how I tried to look at this logically I felt a sense of betrayal.

Charlie had to pass where Annie and I were standing on his way to the gents'. He punched the air to *Rock the Casbah* by the Clash, which was blaring out of the speakers, and barely acknowledged us. This was out of character. Was he *trying* to make me jealous or was he really as oblivious as he seemed? By time he was on his way back I'd decided I'd had enough. As he tried to swan past me in the same manner as earlier, I grabbed him by the arm – something that shocks me now, as I would never normally do that. I can't even remember what I said to him. Something trivial but friendly enough – it was simply my way of saying, *I am here and I see you. What are you playing at?* He wasn't interested. He said something vague back to me and just bounded off. I was in pieces. This was the first time that Charlie had seemingly torn me to shreds, and it wouldn't be the last, unfortunately. Soon after that, saddened and confused, Annie and I left.

Dredging up these memories isn't enjoyable, but in deciding to attempt to capture this long and winding story I know the only way to tell it is with brutal honesty. The path I walked, I sometimes crawled. I could skip along on brighter days, like a bubbling brook bursting with life. Loving this man was a glorious and beautiful thing. I really did believe myself lucky to have met him, but the darker days were part and parcel of the experience too, so it seemed. Some say your soul chooses these meetings way before you're born. That's not something that can be proven or disproven but I can feel my soul both flinching and swelling with joy at the mention of his name. Did it have to be this way? Did this happen because it was supposed to, because it had to, because I chose it, because we chose it? I'll never know for sure. And even if we did choose it, were we allowed to back out? Cancel the flight? Change destinations? I always felt all roads would somehow lead back to Charlie, but I also felt they could take some major detours, and it could be that one or the other of us would get lost and never get back on track. Or some huge, insurmountable roadblock would force us down different highways and byways, but eventually... yeah, it felt that eventually we'd still wind up staring into each other's eyes at the end of the road. And what then? Besides, is there such a thing as the end of the road?

I did too much thinking.

Eleven

Seeing myself in my mind's eye, seven years ago, writhing in pain on that Saturday night, I realise what a wounded person I must have been. Yet, I don't think I was any more wounded than the next person. I've come to feel that we all have many wounds, often hiding beneath the surface, some lurking from this life, some from previous lives and times. Some can be buried so deep we aren't consciously aware of them until they are triggered. These wounds can get reopened many times before they can heal. This process was in full swing now, and much as that night felt like a swift kick in the teeth, in some way it was necessary.

I spoke to Zharha for the third time soon after that event. I wanted some answers because this wasn't making sense to me. One day I'd realise it didn't have to make sense, but I was nowhere near that conclusion that summer. Zharha soon put me straight.

"First off, this *isn't* a new girlfriend," she told me. "She's not *half* the woman you are and he knows it." She proceeded to tell me that Charlie was scared and shocked about how he felt for me – so much more than he expected he would, like it had all just blown up out of nowhere. She also mentioned that he was worried that he couldn't live up to the expectations he perceived that I had.

Whether she was right or wrong is impossible to

say. I understood intellectually what she was saying but I couldn't at that point appreciate the shedload of expectations I'd unconsciously heaped on him. It was so hard to explain as I loved him just the way he was, no doubt about it, but for some reason I also saw his highest potential, a spectrum of full vivid colour that wasn't shut off the way it is in some folks. By the same token, meeting him had awakened me to my *own* full colour spectrum, maybe in the same way. I knew I wasn't lighting up even half the lights on my cosmic dashboard right now. Perhaps I was seeing Charlie's true self, his higher self, even though I wasn't even sure what that meant? Mostly these impulses and expectations were unconscious. I didn't even know I was doing it. And whatever he was doing was pressing my buttons, but he probably didn't know he was doing it either. *It* was being done. *It* was happening.

Zharha told me he thought I was "the cat's meow" and his feelings were literally growing by the day. She said he would lay low for a few days after this drunken night and no real harm was done. Her long-range view was the same. She still saw things coming together and told me not to worry about this woman, who meant nothing in grand scheme of things. Seeing as I felt sure there was a grand scheme at work here and had been from the start, I took her word for it. I knew in my heart he had feelings for me, though I still questioned why he hadn't to date come out and said something – but then, nor had I said a word and I knew how strongly I felt. I attempted to stop worrying about *how* it would happen and I cheered up and got back my composure and my smile.

Charlie wasn't the only good thing in my life, though I can see how these ramblings paint a picture of a woman with a one-track mind. Although my life didn't revolve around Charlie it's also true that he was never far from my thoughts. Never. It was strange and I'd never experienced that with any other person for such a long stretch of time. Never. And I just can't say if I ever will with any other person at this point. So far, only he seems to have this peculiar longevity that simply refuses to fade.

My work kept me busy and I was thankful for that. I loved writing and had from as soon as I could pencil spindly letters on paper as a little girl. Hours were spent weaving stories in my room. There were casts of characters, dramatic as well as mundane plots. It was an avenue that brought me delight and determination. I wrote with a discipline perhaps unusual for a small child but never thought twice about it. It was just something I did. So marrying my love of theatre and writing for *South of the River* was hugely exciting for me. The people I met were generally interesting and unconventional and there were perhaps too many reasons to sit, drink and chat, to burn the stage-and-screen candle at both ends. But this was the life I wanted, even though I probably needed to take a healthier approach. However, there's a lot to be said for doing what you love. Passion for life is good for the physical body as well as the soul.

The connections between body and soul were starting to come more into focus, but at this point I wasn't actively joining the dots that were lining up all over the Universe, like beckoning stars. I had yet to turn them into meaningful constellations. Some twinkled more brightly than others, some appeared most nights, some aligned on rarer, special occasions but all were telling stories, emitting frequencies with cause and effect. At some level, I accepted I was involved in some kind of metaphysical journey that I'd perhaps signed up for during a dream. I wasn't surprised to find myself in it any more. And for the most part, I found it exciting, even if it was often overwhelming and bewildering.

Summer swam by, with it becoming clearer to me that Charlie was no longer with Elaina, even though gossip still occasionally reached my ears mentioning her as his girlfriend, so it appeared that the coast wasn't clear even though my instinct said she was gone and not coming back. I saw him often that summer and we happily chatted, on and off. I interviewed him and two of the other Last Exit Players for *South of the River*. At times it seemed very clear to me that he had feelings for me. At others I occasionally doubted and second-guessed myself and thought perhaps he liked me no more than any girl he saw about town and he was just being friendly. Even a brief recollection of our encounters to date soon put that idea to bed. No, he was feeling this too. I was sure of it, but I still questioned it because it felt too good to be true, and because… well, why wasn't anything happening?

Quantum physicists might be able to explain what I'm about to describe, but in my life experience to date I had never come across this particular phenomenon until I moved to London and Charlie arrived on the scene. Annie and I jokingly called the phenomenon 'duplication' – a term we started to use when somebody appeared to be in two different places at the same time. Largely it was me that witnessed the bulk of these inexplicable happenings but Annie saw a few too. Naturally, the first person to do it was Charlie.

We'd been in London probably less than a year and I knew Charlie reasonably well at this point. Annie and I were going into central London to see a band at the Highbury Garage. As we walked to the Tube station we passed Cafe Noir.

As is commonly the case when Charlie is close by, something pulls me to look in a certain direction. I turn my head and look through the big glass windows at the front of the bar. Yes, there's Charlie, right at the window, with a group of people, looking like he's having a good time. Good, OK, nothing odd about that. We walk on towards the Tube station, but a few moments later my heart starts banging in my chest as we see Charlie approaching us from the direction of the Tube station.

"I don't believe it," I mutter to Annie, who is equally gobsmacked. Within seconds we arrive at the same spot to pass each other.

"Evening." He nods and we greet him as normally as possible. He looks paler than normal, slightly ghostly, pulling on a cigarette in his own inimitable, cool 'Gitane' style. It is undeniably him, and despite his pallor, definitely flesh and blood.

"OK, hang on a minute," I say to Annie when he's walked on and we get to the Tube station. "How on earth do you explain that?"

Obviously we can't explain it. The only way to explain it is that I was mistaken and it wasn't him in Cafe Noir. But it *was*! I knew it was.

I was a little shaken by this but I hurled it away in that box in the corner of my mind, that box that was expanding into a treasure chest of unexplainable, supernatural oddities.

Another example of duplication that stands out for me involved Jay. This time I was walking from Balham Tube station on my way home and bumped into Jay walking into the Tube station just as I was coming out. At this point Jay also lived on Ramsden Road, just a few doors down from the flat I shared with Annie. We greeted each other smilingly and Jay moved on through the barrier whilst I carried on out of the station.

As soon as I got back to the flat I went about opening all the windows, as it was a hot and sticky day. As I opened my bedroom window I was aware that someone was having a phone conversation down below on the street, just beneath the window. I paused as I recognised the voice and then froze, realising the impossibility of what was occurring. It was Jay on his mobile, stood by a car, wearing the same white T-shirt he was wearing when I'd just passed him on the street five minutes before, going into the Tube station. How could this be? If he'd turned around and come back this way I would have seen him as he would have to have overtaken me. Unless he hadn't walked back via the main road I'd just walked? But if he'd gone on some strange ramble through the backstreets he *couldn't* have got there so fast. He gave the impression he'd been there all along. There was no sense that he'd run back and gone straight under the window and got on the phone. Hmm...

Other characters appeared to enact similar scenarios

until it started to become not such a big deal any more, even though I knew it was and I knew it didn't seem to happen except in the area in which we all lived. One evening I popped into the fish and chip shop that was about five minutes from the flat. It was a place I went maybe once a fortnight or so, but the friendly staff knew Annie and me quite well within a short space of time and always chatted cheerily when either of us came in.

As my order was being dished up, the Greek lady who normally served me exclaimed, "Ah! I saw you yesterday."

I was a little surprised. Yesterday I'd spent all day at *South of the River* HQ and went straight home from there. I hadn't been anywhere near the chip shop so I assumed she'd seen me someplace else.

"Oh, where?" I asked.

"Oh, just walking by, on the opposite side of the road," the lady told me casually whilst showering my chips with salt and vinegar.

"Oh... right," I found myself saying uneasily but something stopped me revealing to her that it couldn't have been me... perhaps because on some level I knew she was telling the truth, that she *had* seen me. In my mind, I could see myself walking by exactly as she described even though I knew I hadn't been – or at least, *this* version of me hadn't been. But as I knew it could happen, I reasoned, why should I be immune to the duplication phenomenon?

What did it all mean? It meant either all these sightings were cases of mistaken identity *or* there is such thing as a doppelgänger *or* such a thing as parallel universes – or some other complicated paranormal explanation. Meeting Charlie had cracked my heart right open but the weird goings-on I'd experienced since meeting him, whether connected or not, had cracked my head wide open too – my belief system had been blown to pieces and replaced with massive question marks, exclamation marks and enigmatic ellipses. Things that had seemed implausible suddenly were perfectly plausible. The mysterious workings of the Universe were right on my doorstep – not confined to science fiction programmes or Area 51 in Nevada. In short, there was much more to life than the stuff that met the eye and what didn't meet the eye – and what might have met the eye. My understanding of it all was clumsy and unclear but I was starting to understand that the day-to-day, low style living many of us experience is light years away from our true potential of how we might live, as well as why we are here and what is really going on.

Twelve

A bank holiday weekend, Annie was away and I was hanging out with some members of another group of actors called Ripped Cellophane Productions. I'd conducted a long, confessional interview with their director recently and they had a play opening at the Young Vic the week after. We were ensconced in a corner of Hudson's Cave on this particular Saturday night. The conversation was cheerful and I was in good spirits.

Suddenly, it was like the sun was swiped out of the sky when I saw Charlie appear with a girl I'd never seen before at his side. I remembered Zharha's words the last time this happened, so I told myself not to jump to conclusions, but as I watched him introduce the girl to Hudson, I feared the worst. Charlie found a seat opposite and slightly up from myself and Ripped Cellophane, who were of course blissfully unaware of my sudden source of anguish. Charlie had a habit of sitting opposite me, or at least positioning himself wherever he had a good view of me. He was a master at this. I was often stunned at how blatantly he did it too. So, this time was no different, other than the highly conspicuous fact that he had an unfamiliar girl sitting with him. They were a little giggly and both seemed happy. I knew, even though I hoped I was wrong, this was a new girlfriend.

An onslaught of emotion started to wash over me, and to frame the scene fittingly, *Nothing Compares 2 U* by Sinead O'Connor shuffled onto the Cave's playlist, heightening my struggle against shedding a tear. I alternated between talking to those at my table in the most normal manner I could and staring, crestfallen, at Charlie and the new girl. My impression of the girl was that she seemed quite young in manner but was probably around his age. That would make them both about a decade younger than me. She was dressed casually in T-shirt and jeans. I didn't get any strong impressions about her at this point other than she seemed a little drunk – not on alcohol, but on his presence and being with him. Perhaps, she was thinking something like, *Ooh, I've bagged an actor! A film star, even! Cool!* That was the kind of almost teenage energy she was emitting, despite not being a teenager.

My instinct was to speak to him. It often is. I felt I had to break through this strange, unexpected presentation. So, on my way to the toilets I stopped by their table and made some polite conversation with Charlie, which was too irrelevant for my brain to retrieve it right now.

I remember him responding with a gushing, "Eileen! Hello!" and introducing the girl to me. "Have you met Danielle?" Of course, he knew I hadn't and I'm really not sure what level of awareness he had as to what this turn of events was doing to me. We shared a few words. Danielle didn't speak while I was there but she stroked the arm of his leather jacket in a way that likely aimed to communicate, *He's mine.* I didn't hover too long and carried on downstairs to the toilets with my head spinning. Something wasn't right about this, but I couldn't really get an angle on it.

A few minutes later, I got back to Ripped Cellophane's table and sat down wondering how to announce that I might have to leave suddenly. I then noticed Charlie and Danielle looked like *they* were about to depart. They did. Their departure was a relief on some level, but a stab simultaneously as I guessed they were going somewhere more exciting – for a romantic dinner, maybe, or even worse, going to have sex.

I tried to participate in the conversation at my table but it was hard to focus. This new development was not what I expected, especially with how close Charlie and I had seemed to be getting over the previous weeks.

It was only two days until I saw them again. At least I was half-expecting it this time. It was now the last day of the bank holiday weekend and people seemed to be out in crowds, boozing to obliterate the impending back-to-work inevitability that lurked around the corner. Charlie and Danielle and a group of his friends were already in Hudson's Cave when I walked in. As soon as I saw him – and Danielle – I wished I hadn't, but I forced myself to look. He was a little drunk and so was she. This time it seemed to be via alcohol rather than infatuation. Even though I kept my distance they – or perhaps specifically he – found his way towards me so that he was never far from my side. Charlie seemed to be lining people up as though to make a chain and then bashing into them in a childish way I'd never really seen before. I'd seen him larking around loads but usually in an entertaining way. This just seemed like a silly playground game. Danielle was clinging limply to him again. I couldn't really stomach watching. I had a brief drink and chat with the friend I'd arranged to meet there, then made my excuses and left in as matter-of-fact a way as I could manage. I walked carefully home. *Just put one foot in front of the other. You can do this. You can handle this. You can.*

Though I wasn't, as yet, over-analysing, my instinct told me these two encounters were some kind of performance, though I'm not exactly sure who was performing for whom or why. But really, what did I know? I was just an observer and arguably a very subjective one. And perhaps it was really none of my business. After seeing them together twice I had no doubt she was a new girlfriend. I remember even enquiring with Hudson to make sure I had my facts right. I always wanted facts. I could handle the truth but much of the time, since my arrival in Balham, things seemed so nebulous and contradictory I was left scratching my head.

"So Charlie has a new girlfriend?" I'd asked Hudson in my straightforward style that can occasionally freak people out.

"Er, yes," the normally unflappable Hudson said nervously.

"So, it's over with Elaina?" I clarified.

"Yes," replied Hudson, looking like he was a little scared that I might throw a chair across the bar.

"Oh right, OK," was all I said, and I didn't mention it again. What Hudson knew about my feelings for Charlie I'll never know, but perhaps you'd have to be blind not to see Charlie had my heart. I never knew how obvious I was. I never knew how obvious *he* was, but I knew how obvious he seemed to me. But here was the puzzle. If this was mutual, if this was so obvious, why was Charlie with someone new?

74

My head and heart were in a spin but somehow there wasn't the same anger and sense of betrayal I'd felt on the night a few months before when he'd been with another. My gut was saying this wasn't a big deal and this twist in the tale would iron itself out and blow away. Maybe it was just a fling or possibly even an attempt to make me jealous, though I wasn't sure Charlie was the type to play those kinds of games. Still, for whatever reason, as time went on, it just didn't appear that his heart was especially engaged with his new lady.

I couldn't get hold of Zharha for a few weeks to get her take on the new developments. I knew she would be straight with me. I knew I had a lot of emotion invested in the situation and I could be misreading things. What struck me as strange was that Danielle appeared to cling to him, to seem wary and on edge and not to let him out of her sight. It seemed odd for a new relationship but there could be all kinds of reasons for this, and I tried not to make judgements.

When I finally did get hold of Zharha a few weeks later, she wasn't even inclined to discuss it. She said it was "nothing". She said to treat it as nothing. There was nothing to worry about. Things would progress. She told me to keep the faith and carry on as normal. So I did. I tried not to focus too much on them, but of course I was looking out of the corner of my eye. I got on with things, noticing that oddly, my heart wasn't breaking like I would have expected it to. Perhaps that was because Charlie continued to flirt with me, right under Danielle's nose.

Thirteen

You know I said my world had become more weird and wizardly since I'd arrived in London? There's a scene around this juncture that sticks in my head, demonstrating this very clearly. *South of the River* were heading further south and doing a couple of nights in Brighton as part of the Brighton Festival, and guess which group of actors were on the bill? As it was partly being organised by me, Charlie had the charming audacity to ask me to organise a coach to get the local fan base down. I agreed. We had quite a lot of discussion about ways of promoting the performance and I remember Danielle seeming put out by his frequent interactions with me. I suppose she wondered what the hell was between us. Were we really just friends? That was a good question.

There was a man who hung around the streets of Balham, Tooting and Clapham Junction who sat on street corners, drinking cider and muttering – or sometimes shouting, or sometimes speaking in a fairly normal tone of voice. On more than one occasion he'd blurted out something eerily topical when I'd passed him on the street. Annie and I dubbed him the 'manic street preacher', and though we weren't entirely serious about his prophetic abilities we weren't dismissive of them either.

I remember after leaving Hudson's Cave with thoughts

of coach organisation in my head, walking the distance home and passing the manic street preacher, who, to my astonishment, exclaimed as I walked by, "We're all going to Brighton!" I did a double take and carried on walking. How on earth did he know that? He hadn't been anywhere near when the discussion was happening. He randomly delivered messages like this, though. He was part of the crazy world I now occupied, where telepathy and bilocation were by no means unusual.

Activity shook up around October. The Last Exit Players were having some complications with their rehearsal space and were struggling to fund the cost of maintaining it as the owner of the rooms kept hiking up the rent. Charlie had agreed to have a chat with me for *South of the River* about a potential new production, the film he'd made in Wales that was still awaiting release but looked closer to finding a distributor. This was, of course, business rather than personal and I always made sure I kept in professional mode in these situations. Having said that, I can't pretend I wasn't looking forward to some time alone with him. The arrival of Danielle had clouded things and I welcomed a chance for us to perhaps clear the confusion a little.

Instead, those vague clouds gathered energy and emerged as storm clouds. Charlie didn't show for a meeting we'd arranged at Hudson's Cave. I told myself he was just late and he'd bounce in the door at any minute. After fifteen minutes or so I tried phoning him. No reply. I waited a little longer, then anxiously tried again. No reply. Hudson seemed strangely sympathetic to my distress, which I *thought* I was keeping in check – but it was probably leaking all over those Guinness beer mats I was tearing up and making jagged jigsaw pieces with. Hudson told me to phone Thomas, another member of the Last Exit Players. I wasn't sure why he suggested that, but I wasn't in the mood to question, so I called Thomas.

"Eileen, hello. What's wrong?" Thomas said worriedly.

"I was supposed to meet Charlie at the Cave. Hudson gave me your number and said you might know where he is," I found myself saying, trying to keep it together and casual-seeming, rather than deranged, which is how I worried I came across. Thomas said he didn't know where Charlie was (why would he?) but he'd try ringing him and let me know if he got any info. I thanked him and told Hudson I was going home.

"If Charlie turns up, can you ask him to ring me?" I said with as much dignity as I could muster, and escaped back to the flat.

Once inside, the floodgates opened and hot and hurt tears rolled quickly down my cheeks. I was lucky I had such a kind flatmate. Annie listened and didn't judge. She was a comfort and I was grateful. Still, there was no getting away from the fact that my heart was hurting badly. It worried me how much it hurt. It seemed over-the-top, the acuteness of the pain. Perhaps it was a delayed reaction to the whole Danielle thing. I was shocked that Charlie had let me down and not even picked up the phone. Nobody likes being let down but if this had been anyone but Charlie a situation such as this wouldn't have equalled such a steep level of devastation. I would simply have been a little frustrated and shrugged it off. Was it because I thought he didn't care after all? Had it tainted my idealistic image of him, perhaps? I never thought Charlie would hurt me intentionally. The trouble was that everything involving this man hit me so very personally. It was like I had no armour where he was concerned. Had I always been a quivering emotional wreck or had he triggered some strange abandonment issue in me? Clearly he triggered strong responses in me. It was as though everything that happened between us was amplified – the ups were higher and lows were deeper, and all sensations were stronger and sharper. Somehow, I got through the pain but I was concerned about the intensity of it all. Once again, nothing made sense.

A few nights later, Annie and I went to the cinema, after which I had a strange compulsion to pop into Hudson's Cave for a quick drink. It wasn't a conscious urge and it was usually very subtle, but many times, since my arrival in London, I was propelled to go places, as though being led by a gentle guiding breeze. That night was one of them and as soon as I pushed the creaking door open and stepped into the bar I could see why.

Charlie.

He turned his head to see who'd stepped in, and on seeing me he literally sprang to my side. "Eileen, Eileen, Eileen, Eileen, *Eileen!*" It was almost a chant, a spine-tingling repetition of my name. He wasted no time in telling me that Hudson and Thomas had been berating him for letting me down. His speech was passionate and powerful, leaving barely space for me to breathe, let alone speak. "If you think I'd ever intentionally blow you out then you're mistaken. I would never, never intentionally do that to you," he declared. Next thing I knew he was down on his knees, looking up at me imploringly, saying, "God strike me down if I don't mean it!" I was too stunned to know what to do or think. It was obvious he meant it. A small audience hanging round the bar were silently watching this performance and I was dimly aware that Danielle was sitting on a sofa watching too, far away enough not to be able to hear his words.

As I looked down at him, I couldn't bear it. I was plunged into a peculiar sense of déjà vu, which felt unsettling. Something flashed before my eyes like a ripple from another place and time when we'd been in these same positions – him down on his knees, either begging for mercy or declaring love. I didn't know which and it didn't matter, as I'm sure it was both at one time or another. I also felt we were probably in reverse positions, with me on my knees, at yet another time. I told him to get up. In fact, I half-pulled him up. I didn't like the disparity between us. I didn't understand what had just happened but it felt like we'd just re-enacted something from a past life – a dizzying yanking back and forth across different time zones. I told him all was OK and he was forgiven or words to that effect. I don't remember what I said. I just wanted him to stand up and stop pulling on my heartstrings. He quietly arose, seeming unaware of the audience or the magnitude of his demonstration. I watched him return unenthusiastically to Danielle and give her a quick peck on the cheek. She didn't look too happy, understandably.

I heard him telling her loudly, "Eileen is writing a piece about Last Exit Players in South of the River", as though that was a rational explanation or excuse for his overly demonstrative behaviour. I'll never forget that night. It proved to me, if you can prove such a thing, that he cared deeply.

Soon after, we made plans to do the interview we had been going to do. Charlie and I initially met in Hudson's Cave as usual, but we decided to go to a place called Ceiling for our chat. Christmas was drawing near and I remember brushing past twinkling trees outside the welcoming doors of Ceiling, a new, upmarket bar with mirrors on a portion of the high ceilings and psychedelic paintings on the rest. One of Charlie's long-term friends, Keith, was with him that night. He often had a friend in tow in those days. Keith chattered away to me while we waited at the bar to be served.

I soon became aware that Danielle was also sitting in the bar with a few friends. This irked me a little. Not because I was jealous, but because Charlie was officially 'working' when doing an interview with the magazine; even if sitting and having a drink with me wasn't exactly hard work, I saw this as a professional engagement despite my personal feelings and somehow it didn't feel quite right that his girlfriend was hanging around waiting for him to finish. My instinct was that she had invited herself along rather than him asking her. At any rate, there was nothing I could do about it. I was relieved that when we'd got our drinks he walked me over to a corner table for two so we could conduct the interview in private.

I set up my recording equipment and we were away. Words were never a problem between us in situations like this. Charlie was a great interviewee. He had plenty to say and our wavelength was perfect.

Yet, strangeness occurred within five minutes. The

81

lighting flickered and we were suddenly plunged into semi-darkness. Nearby staff tried to fix things by playing around with some trip switches in a box beside us. But it seemed we had a power cut. Charlie and I giggled and grinned at each other. We could still see each other perfectly well by candlelight and I fully admit there was nothing in the world I wanted to do more than stay and chat, or just stare into his beautiful eyes, but management were making noises about health and safety and having to evacuate the premises. We decided to call the interview off.

He excused himself, saying with a kind of resigned reluctance, "I guess I better go and see my bird!"

What could I say? "OK!"

We both got up and he wandered in Danielle's direction, and I moved towards the door. She met him halfway and literally grabbed his arm, pulling him to a seating position on a sofa. Awkwardly, Charlie waved and called goodbye to me, a helpless look spreading across his face. It was a look I was going to see many times over the coming years, a sort of apologetic shrug that told me he didn't want things to be like this but that the alternative was too... difficult?

By time I got out on the street the electricity had reconnected and Ceiling was once again brightly illuminated. I decided against re-entering and attempting to resurrect the interview. We'd find another time. I walked home and reported my strange evening to Annie. I was glad she agreed with me that it was odd that Danielle had been in the house at all when she knew he was out to do an interview, as I had wondered if I was overreacting. We also remarked on the weirdness of the timing of the power cut. Those few moments we had spent together had shown me once again how magically charged the air was when we were together. There was a sense of both belonging and excitement, and I had to keep myself in check, hoping my hands weren't shaking when I switched on the tape recorder or that I wasn't blabbering nonsensically with nervous energy. It was like the evening had been snatched out of my hands for no reason I could understand. Yet at the same time I knew there was some kind of cosmic reason.

I knew by now that where dealings with Charlie were concerned timing seemed to play a more pertinent role than usual. At times, things were liable to stop dead in their tracks without explanation. At other times, mountains could be suddenly moved, if it seemed necessary. There was a sense of some higher power being in operation to ensure things occurred at precise points in time. In other words, universal or divine timing, call it what you will, was steering this thing along, but of course, I wanted things to run on my timing. Who doesn't? I replayed the strange happenings as I lay in bed that night, feeling frustrated, aching for a chance to spend some time with Charlie where we could melt into each other in the delicious way we had seemed just about to when the power cut had struck. I had no choice but to accept that right now, for whatever multitude of reasons, we couldn't be together and maybe we never would be. It didn't stop me wanting it, though.

Fourteen

I saw Charlie very soon after that night and was glad he seemed keen to reschedule our interview. He had three performances with the Last Exit Players coming up before Christmas, doing a modern-day, anti-capitalist rewrite of Dickens' *A Christmas Carol*, so we agreed to leave our chat until the festive season was over as we were both going away to see family. I did see Charlie a few nights before I left for Manchester though, at the *South of the River* Christmas party. He'd accepted my invitation to perform a scene from the *Christmas Carol* play at the party, as it had been such a resounding success. A few other local performance groups, dancers and musicians were also involved. The magazine always had a Christmas party and it was a feel-good night on the annual theatrical calendar, bringing together, under one occasionally snow-capped roof, a lively cross-section of actors, playwrights and film business people draped in tinsel and sparkly attire.

South of the River staff took stints on the door, checking off names against the extensive guest list and greeting the largely smiling party people who swished in and out the doors. Somebody arrived who wasn't smiling. It was Danielle. This was possibly the first time we'd ever had any real interaction as opposed to just warily observing each other, and sadly it wasn't pretty. Charlie had given me several names of girls who were friends of hers for the guest list. I'd carefully put their tickets into festive-looking green and red envelopes with their names clearly written on each one.

I was taken aback when Danielle started snatching the envelopes out of my hand, and correcting me because one of the names didn't match who was actually coming. It was a tense and embarrassing encounter. I made sure all her friends got in – that was never an issue or problem. The problem I experienced was with her rather aggressive attitude, and I felt upset afterwards. Logically, I shouldn't have let it get to me but I hadn't been prepared for such an obvious demonstration of hostility. Of course, Charlie knew nothing of it, as I'm sure it would have embarrassed him equally. I mentioned it to one of the bar staff with whom I was quite friendly and who happened to be nearby, just to get it out of my system.

"Oh, she's like that with everyone," he said dismissively. "Don't let it bother you, Eileen." So, perhaps it wasn't as personal as it felt. I knew it wasn't really worth getting upset about, so somehow I smoothed out my energy and got on with the night.

I could paint detailed pictures of each encounter I had with Charlie and Danielle over the coming months, but most of them went along similar lines, with similar energy. I sensed I was a source of friction for them, which I guessed was largely because of the connection I shared with Charlie, even though I certainly never intended to cause trouble between them. Equally, though, I wasn't prepared to break off my friendship with Charlie just because of Danielle's disapproval. I was always respectful of his choices, even if I wished they were different and I can't pretend I didn't wish they were different. But I knew I had to find a sense of grace here, a sense of acceptance and trust that this all had a greater purpose. Through my eyes, it seemed that the Universe had put this man on my path for some mighty reason – and I was still trying to figure out what that was, what my role was. We'd found companionship and a closeness that was special, but somehow we both struggled to dare name what was between us. Time and again we'd be in the same public place, each trailing the other with our eyes and pretending we weren't, each trying to be casual when feeling anything but, each perhaps trying to make sense and finding anything but. The arrival of Danielle and the fact that she was still around six months later should have put a stop to the yearnings of my heart; to the messages I was still receiving in signs and synchronicities. *If Charlie is the one, if he feels the same, which I still feel he does deep down, why isn't he with me?* I'd ask myself. I could find lots of possible answers but none that really stopped the searching feeling, the confusion or apparent absurdity of my life during those days.

Around this juncture I remember a particular dream, and also the sensation of it. The setting of the dream was Hudson's Cave, and both Charlie and I were on the stage. He was lying on top of me. I suppose we were in the missionary position but we weren't having traditional sex, just writhing around a bit and he was repeating this phrase, "It's never going to end, it's never going to end, it's never going to end, it's never going to end", over and over and over again. There was a strong sense of rhythm to the whole thing; the phrase had a very even rhythm and so did our movements. The strange thing was, even though he was lying on top of me and there was no way I could move, he was remarkably gentle and careful. There was nothing forceful about it, even though it may sound that way when I describe him pinning me to the floor. It was as though he was stating a fact – that 'it' was eternal and that 'it' was something beyond our control. I didn't speak as far as I remember. I was at his mercy, but I was in safe, loving hands and I knew it. I also sensed he was right. It was never going to end.

I remember waking from the dream and still feeling the weight of Charlie's body on mine, like a phantom indent on my skin. Although I was astounded on some level I was also not freaked out by it because I knew how utterly real the dream had felt, and indeed many dreams I'd had of him both before and after this one were just as tangible as everyday life. Still, this was a particularly striking dream and even now, years later, I can hear that mantra. I can feel the coolness of the floor of the stage under my back. I can feel his body on mine and hear his voice in my ear. It doesn't scare me. It's just… the way it is.

I did wonder if Charlie shared some of these dreams with me. I knew on some level he *must* because he was so *present*, it had to be his essence that travelled to me at night just as mine must surely be travelling to him – but how much did he remember or take notice of? If I've inhabited his dreams as much as he has mine over the years it must be somewhat disconcerting for him being in a relationship with someone else. There have been times where the dreams felt haunting but also times where they felt truly comforting, where I felt enveloped by his love. Perhaps it was the same for him. I didn't know because I never felt I could ask. I do remember a time he mentioned a dream when we were in Hudson's Cave, but almost as soon as he started telling it to me he kind of wrapped it up and put it away again worriedly, as though he'd realised mid-speech that if he told me he'd been dreaming of me and what had happened it could be too revealing, a confession almost. I understood and didn't press him.

Fifteen

Early one spring day, I checked in with Zharha. This consultation was over the phone as she'd told me we could work that way equally well. We hadn't spoken for a while and I was, once again, having a hard time making sense of things. That day began a process that in many ways is still ongoing, though I don't require her help any more, thankfully. She first used a term that day that I'd never heard before and didn't really take on board, despite recognising immediately that it rang a deep-seated bell with me.

"I do understand what this means to both of you. Being twin flames (which you are) means that it is so close of a connection that it is uncomfortable to be together at times... So close that the fear that you two can see right through each other is scary."

Twin flames? It was an important-sounding description or phenomenon, but I had no real understanding of what it meant. I knew it *sounded* right. I knew she was talking of something rare, but for whatever reason, I didn't question the term or explore it at that point. Still, on some level it had seeped into my psyche and I let it rest there, somewhere around my heart. That day Zharha decided to do some energy work that would help me establish and maintain balance. I kiss the day she opened that door for me despite the fact that much of it pulled up tons of buried emotional junk, leaving me to wade through the murk of yesteryear. Scars surfaced but so did stars, brighter, more dazzling stars than I could ever have imagined. They say when the student is ready, the teacher appears. My teacher couldn't have been more perfect for me. Somehow she had walked similar roads. She was incredibly generous with the time and energy she devoted to my path and my issues. She believed in Charlie and me and our being together, but more than that, she so believed in me and what was best for me, even if that meant *not* being with Charlie, and though the thought of that was enough to make my very soul cry, I knew if it truly *was* for the best that we remain apart, Zharha was the person who could help me through that. This remarkable woman was a teacher, mentor and cherished friend and I knew I was lucky to have found her.

Zharha's work aimed to get me into balance, and it did. Obviously I didn't become completely balanced overnight but within weeks I was starting to feel different. She worked to unblock chakras, untie knots, smooth out tangles. It was really a kind of spring clean of the full anatomy of my soul. Bit by bit, each crevice of my being yielded up the accumulated gunk and stored trauma. This process went on for years. It's still going on now because we never stop learning, and just as you have to keep physically active to keep physically fit, you have to work with meditation and awareness to keep energetically balanced. These days I'm definitely carrying less dense debris than I was and I'm capable of releasing my junk on my own. Sometimes I fought it; sometimes I welcomed it. Like an unpolished precious stone that had been soaking in an emotional oil slick, it took a lot of washing, scrubbing, exfoliating and moisturising to get that stone to shine. Now it gleams in the sunlight, sparkles in the moonlight, and though the everyday knocks of life can chip it, bruise it and sully it at times, it's so much easier now to wash it clean again. I'd always been open to the idea that remote healing worked, but after a few sessions with Zharha, I had no doubt. This wasn't about me remaining passive, though. I had to do the work and she helped me through it. What's more, I began to understand that I could facilitate healing too. It was the start of a whole new phase of my life. I was hugely excited by the realisation and understanding that we are energetic beings. Yes, we are flesh and blood but we are *so* much more.

The combination of meeting Charlie and then having Zharha to guide me through the web woven between and around us was a crash course in energy work, physics, chemistry, mysticism and pure magic. Zharha spoke often about the pull between us. I knew this pull existed very early on, perhaps even before we physically met.

Remember those visions I'd had of him when leaving Manchester – before ever even meeting him? There was no one else in the world that seemed capable of 'pulling' me the way Charlie did. It literally seemed to be a magnetic force, a very strong one, one that actually didn't seem capable of being broken. It took me years to come to terms with that. Once I did, I learned that all I had to do was accept this connection as a gift from the Universe – because really, that's what it was, what it still is. Rather than see it as a relentless and restrictive pull, it was about seeing it as a precious lesson in love. The bond would always be there but I didn't have to be at its mercy, and we didn't have to be together for either of us to be whole and happy – though being together was always an option at the same time. The lesson, or part of it at least, was about being whole and happy within myself and not looking to anyone else to fulfil that perceived lack or need – to understand that love isn't about need, but actually about *not* needing, about loving unconditionally. But as I say, I spent years trying to get my head around it – in fact, you *can't* get your head around it. It's not something the brain can fathom. I now recognise that this magnetic force was stronger than either of us. I see it as an example of the infallible mechanics of the Universe, making sure that I paid attention, making sure I noticed the magnitude of this so I could learn something, so he could perhaps learn something too, so we could grow through this incredible connection.

For a long time, we merged energetically in such a way that I literally couldn't separate what was mine and what was his. I'd hear his thoughts, I'd feel his feelings in such a way that made no logical sense – it was as though we lived inside each other, and shared a common core at times. In no way did I really understand all this, or what to do about it back then, but I was grateful to Zharha for starting to peel back each layer of this extraordinary experience. I was learning to navigate a journey I hadn't even chosen consciously. Clearly I knew this was an unusual connection, but I didn't fully grasp that it had happened for a big reason, that it happened to others, that it *would* happen to others. I was still too focused on

Charlie himself – Charlie the flesh-and-blood man with the flashing blue eyes – even though from day one I'd also been aware there was more to this than 'boy meets girl'.

It's bigger than us, was still the whispered refrain I'd hear on the wind, stumble over in the street, tripping me up until I really listened and actually took it on board. I had to look beyond the boy-meets-girl aspect of it... a long way beyond.

I'd shed a lot of skins over the coming years, some I'd fight to keep, as Zharha often told me. I'd cling to the old way that was hurting me out of habit, but as time went on I learned to let each layer go. Breaking ingrained, dysfunctional patterns is scary and difficult but it can be done, and slowly I became aware that I didn't want the old me back, even though it's unnerving to feel the void between the loss of a part of you and the growth or rediscovery of your true self, your ancient and perfect self.

Looking back now, I gasp at how stuck I seemed, how I allowed myself to be tossed and turned on the tide of this thing that literally brought me to my knees. It's easy to think, how could I be so stupid, so apparently masochistic, even? But until I understood the strange dynamics, I was helpless. Until I was prepared to grow and change, I was trapped. I was being pushed to be the better, bigger, brighter version of myself but I had to take on that challenge, to learn to embrace it. It took me a while to learn that I could ride on the roller coaster year in and year out – or I could get off. When you realise there is an exit sign you have to consciously follow it. You have to push open that door and let the other one swing shut. I didn't see I had that option for the longest time, but then perhaps I had to ride the roller coaster long enough to appreciate the benefits of getting off.

What I have learned is that it takes continued application to stay in a healthy zone. For me, at least, there was no arriving at the summit of the mountain and hoisting a victory flag. Life continues to throw pleasure and pain at me along my path but these days I pick each offering up and examine it with as much love and compassion as I can muster, and that includes love for myself. It's still a challenge at times not to peer down the rabbit hole that Charlie's arrival seemed to unearth, but at least I've managed to stop falling head first into it.

Sixteen

Oh, how much I loved him. It was a river-deep, mountain-high kind of love. It had all-encompassing latitude and longitude, magnitude and majesty. Even at a distance if I spied him down the road my heart would pound, my spirit would soar. There would often be that feeling I described before, an urge to run away competing with an urge to run into his arms. It threw my soul into a panic. But usually, once we spoke or came into each other's aura space, that panic lessened. Sometimes it melded into a feeling of peace, of comfort, of bliss. I saw enough of him, even after the arrival of Danielle, to make this a regular occurrence. Some weeks I'd see him nearly every day, sometimes twice a week or so. Occasionally there'd be gaps of a couple of weeks if one or the other of us was away, but it rarely went beyond that. Even a moment with him somehow made everything OK, made me smile, made my life extraordinary.

There was a night that same year, so sweet it was as if an angel had tipped over a casket of the most exquisite perfume, drenching the two of us briefly, leaving its eternal scent, the lingering memory, to soak deep into my soul. Nothing much happened – except a kiss and a long, long, loving look.

Nothing much and everything.

It was Easter Saturday and a kick-ass band from Liverpool were playing in Hudson's Cave. I was waiting to be served at one end of the bar. The place was jam-packed, so the waiting time was longer than normal. As I waited I began to feel I was being watched from the other end of the bar. Watched is an understatement. I felt as though I was being drunk up, every inch of me, devoured with a gaze that spelt love, lust and longing as well as some kind of pulsating, heavenly light that just beamed itself into my heart. The sender was Charlie. *Charlie.* There he stood, staring adoringly at me. Probably, I began to blush. I avoided his eyes. I'm not sure if he was trying to make eye contact or not, but for whatever reason I averted my gaze and concentrated on the transaction with a member of the Cave's bar staff as a way of trying to keep my equilibrium. I could feel him without looking. I could *feel* he was still looking. I'd never felt a man look at me quite like this before. I'm not talking about the normal eyeing-up and nudges and winks that happen when someone takes a fancy to you in a public place. This was in another league. And though there certainly was a sexual element in the mix, that was only one facet of it. The essence of his look was love, amazing love, and it travelled all the way from the far end of the bar to my end, caressing me long-distance. Once I'd been served I stood back, out of his line of vision. Again I don't know why, probably because I could scarcely handle the intensity, even though I was flattered and enormously pleased by it.

It was one of those nights where people were squashed together and it was easier to stay crammed in a corner than move. Wherever I was in the crowd I felt he would've found me. That night Charlie was with Thomas, one of the Last Exit Players. Danielle was nowhere in sight.

He found me and greeted me with a soft-voiced, "Hi, Eileen", and the next thing I knew his lips were on mine. I was so shocked I don't remember how I responded – whether I kissed him back or whether I just froze. After the kiss, he matter-of-factly moved on through the venue towards the stage as though to check out the band. Thomas, who was behind him, flapped around nervously and asked me if I was OK. Did I look that shocked? I said I was fine. I was fine. Thomas moved on too. My head and heart were reeling. That kind of kiss was not of the normal greeting variety, the pecks on the cheek both sexes give each other to say hello. Oh no, it was a *real* kiss. Not only had his lips properly met mine but his arm had grabbed my waist too. I was only aware of that now because I felt the residue of the pressure – and the pleasure. What had got into him? Did he realise what he'd just done? Where was Danielle?

I don't remember much about the rest of the night. I know we passed each other again; I think at the door where one or the other of us was going out, but neither of us spoke. Perhaps this sounds like I'm making a big deal over nothing, just some guy feeling some kind of attraction to me on a particular night – but truly, this was something else. It wasn't just the kiss, it was the *energy*, which was all over the room! It was a major hit, a major happening, a step over an invisible line. Yet, no words were spoken. No words were needed.

That April and May were important in the sense that I learned a lot, got stronger, had relapses, had faith and lost faith almost on a daily basis. I was going round in circles and so was Charlie. Danielle was sometimes absent for stretches of time and I was playing unhealthy guessing games. *Could it be over? Could there be someone else? Could I be wrong? Could I be right? Could it be tomorrow? Could it be never? Have I missed the boat? Is my ship just about to come in? Have I lost the plot?* Around this time, Zharha was unavailable for long stretches of time also due to various personal reasons of her own. She had her own life to live and I learned that I had to go within and find answers for myself at times, or better still, accept that there aren't always answers or even if there are, they won't always be revealed to you if the time isn't right. It was a steep and often painful learning curve I was hoisting myself along.

Possibly due to Zharha's work, possibly due to the energy activation that meeting Charlie had started in me, or a combination of both, I was also experiencing an assortment of odd physical symptoms and ailments. Burning palms, trouble sleeping, headaches, even occasional heart palpitations as well as bursts of high energy and bouts of fatigue. None of these things were extreme, but they were noticeable.

Another episode of duplication occurred around this time involving Charlie. Annie and I had been out someplace I can't recall and were passing Ceiling with its big, wide windows on the way home. Oh no! There were Charlie and Danielle, exhibiting the oddest vibe. I watched in shock seeing Danielle leaning across the table, either scolding Charlie or at the very least making a strong point. He appeared to recoil, his back bending backwards as far he could. Annie and I didn't wait to see any more, but walked on uncomfortably.

We were planning on going into a nearby corner shop for some milk, but as we approached we froze at a distance because outside, standing in the doorway, smoking a cigarette, stood Charlie – or that was certainly what we both believed we saw. A mixture of instinct and fear pulled us back and we cut down a different street, both uttering one of our most commonly used phrases:

"I don't believe it!"

"It was him!"

"It *was* him!"

"But… but how could it be when…?"

"I know, I know, it's not the first time."

"It felt like him."

"It did."

"It was him."

I turned it over and over in my head and somehow my feeling was that Charlie had teleported himself out of the bar and down the road almost as a means of self-protection from whatever was going on back there. I also had this odd feeling that he was trying to show me that the him I'd just seen in Ceiling wasn't the real him… that he wasn't a happy participant in that odd scene and that he'd temporarily vacated the place. Could you do such a thing? I know you can switch yourself off sometimes and imagine you're elsewhere, but can your body *appear* where you've pictured yourself? There was something ghostly about this experience, and it chilled me. Once again, I put it in the box, the heaving box of unexplainable psychic phenomena, the lid of which I was starting to have trouble closing. Annie and I were sensible people. We weren't on drugs. We'd seen this. It was real, whatever real meant.

Seventeen

The Only One I Know by the Charlatans is one of my favourite songs of all time. It was bursting from Ceiling bar one summer evening as I was passing. How could I resist the pull? And I knew instinctively who had flicked on that switch. Charlie had a friend named Louis, who was also an actor but in a more part-time capacity than Charlie. These days he was spending more time working as a DJ. It actually helped pay the bills more easily than relying on acting work, which for Charlie and the other Last Exit Players was often an uncertain and erratic business financially. Charlie would often join Louis when he played around Balham, Brixton or Streatham and sometimes spin a few records himself, though usually he would just be hanging with Louis or other friends, smoking, drinking and chatting. When I heard that Charlatans record it was as though an invisible force had whipped me off the street, and the next thing I knew I was looking into Charlie's dancing eyes whilst Louis looked on knowingly from the decks.

I'd often find myself standing before him and it didn't seem to matter that there wasn't really any reason. I sometimes created one. I don't think he minded. Perhaps it was some kind of energy fix that I craved, almost an addiction on some level. I didn't know how to explain it as I'd never felt this way before, despite believing I'd been in love before. Nothing felt better than being with Charlie for a reason or no reason. It was like all the cells in my body just yelled with pure joy.

But at the end of the day when I walked away, despite the easily available euphoria in many of our exchanges, there was the realisation that Charlie was with someone else.

Somehow his body language never said that to me. Often I actually felt he tried to spare my feelings, sending me silent messages encoded in those pleading looks for understanding. At this stage I didn't trust telepathy as much as I've learned to now, but even then I sometimes got a sense that he was saying, *Wait for me. I'll be with you one of these days. Don't give up on me. Please.* Perhaps I was mistaken, perhaps not.

I knew ultimately it was none of my business what was going on between Charlie and Danielle. We never discussed it. It was rare that he even mentioned her. I witnessed many scenes where he appeared disinterested in her but I told myself I didn't know the full story, which of course I didn't, chiding myself for even wondering about it – but naturally I did wonder about it. What was undeniable to my soul was that whatever this thing was between Charlie and me, it wasn't dissipating. The spark remained, through thick and thin. I'd catch him staring at me, searching me out and sending those signals that bounced around my heart anxiously. Living like this wasn't healthy but I seemed powerless to stop loving him or wanting him. So, I carried on and weeks turned into months, which would eventually down the line turn into years. We still weren't together and Danielle was still in the picture. The picture wasn't really changing one way or another. They moved in together. That was a blow, and though the blows kept coming my heart just wouldn't let go.

It was that summer that I first decided to embark on my journey into learning a thing or two about healing. This took the form of attending a Reiki level one course over a weekend in a twisty-twirly house in Wimbledon – water fountains tinkled in various corners and the vaguely yellow, sun-infused air was tingling with a subtle but peaceful energy that wasn't unfamiliar to me. Through an ancient Japanese ritual I was attuned to Reiki and was told that from this point on Reiki would flow through me to heal and help whenever I called upon it, in such a way that was for the greatest good of all concerned, so it was also a lesson in learning to leave expectations at the door, to trust that what I wanted to happen might not be what was best for me or whoever I was hoping to heal. And that was a big deal because even though I could accept that in principle, expectations had a habit of creeping in through the back door.

I felt heat emitting from my palms when I intended to heal. It seemed quite clear that something was going on and this wasn't all in my head. Something had been activated, or perhaps I should say reactivated because this energy didn't feel completely new to me. I couldn't exactly explain what had led me to be sitting in that house in Wimbledon. I somehow sensed that if I hadn't met Charlie I probably wouldn't be there. Perhaps it was through feeling the power of Zharha's energy work, which was by her own admission a mishmash of the best of each healing modality she had trained in, but melded with her own very special signature. It was an almost unconscious decision. I felt propelled to explore that world. I wasn't even sure how much I wanted to, but a quiet knock had been sounding in my psyche for some time, nudging me to do something of this nature. I finally relented. My life didn't change dramatically and I understood that I needed to do further training to be really proficient in it. I felt I'd taken a first step, or perhaps semi-staggered towards the light. My aim was primarily to heal others but I quickly learned that healing the self had to come first and foremost. It was as though all my wounds were rising to the surface, like craters on a drought-stricken land, waving for water.

Once this process began, there was no going back, or any attempt to do so would have been in vain. On some deep level I knew this, which may be why I took my time in taking the plunge. On a soul level I'd decided that I'd look each issue in the eye, see it for what it was, and search for a way forwards. I was no longer content to cower behind my fears, to be at their mercy. I was going to face myself, and everything else, one step at a time.

I had a job to do that wasn't entirely clear to me, but it was a job that pulled me onwards, through a maze of emotions and memories, a desire to understand why we suffer, why we hurt, how we can heal, how we can't just put a bandage on a wound but that there are ways to bring about resolution, to knit the fabric back together so it's as good as new, clean, regenerated, free to breathe and smile again.

Some days I truly felt wonderful. It was by no means

all pain and purging. And all this time Charlie remained in my heart, tugging it, swelling it, making it bang like a drum, making it burst with love or constrict with pain. There was no stopping this thing. He was part of every day, whether I saw him or not, and most days, at this point, he'd pop up here or there and those times together, whether brief or extended, meant so much to me. In more recent days, years later, when I rarely saw him, those times seemed even more precious and I wish I'd not spent so much time fretting about the future instead of enjoying the present... but then, that was one my lessons and my cosmic educators were patient but firm. They wanted me to learn, but I kept getting in my own way at this point. I was too focused on Charlie rather than what he had come to show me, too caught up in the trappings of romance and failing to see that though this was a romance, it wasn't a normal one. Normality as I'd known it would never exist again, which was a blessing but not something that was making sense. Things making sense would happen less and less too, but I wasn't prepared to accept that yet either. I was learning and I'd make little leaps here and there, but the bigger leaps, the leaps of no return, were yet to come.

Eighteen

There was an evening that summer when both Charlie and Jason had come round to my flat for an interview for the magazine. They'd been on a trip to New York where Charlie had performed in the Fringe NYC festival and Jay had been doing some film work. Naturally they were both buzzing from this, full of tall tales and different tempos. We sat in the slightly poky front room in the flat on Ramsden Road which Annie and I still shared, even though we were tiring of its pokiness and electrical faults and looking to move. Annie was away with other friends back up north. We talked for a long time about New York, about the Last Exit Players, about theatre and film, about anything and everything. We sipped red wine and general giddiness was in the air.

I remember Charlie going down on his knees to me again that night. It bothered me less than it did that first time in Hudson's Cave, but I still found it an over-the-top gesture in the circumstances. It was his way of thanking me for the preliminary script I'd recently sent him of a play I'd been writing for the Last Exit Players, which he clearly loved. I had that same impulse to get him to stand up immediately. I also wondered what on earth Jay must be thinking – but then I'd thought that many times.

Jay had witnessed many of our encounters and he

couldn't have missed some of the exuberance and intensity emitting from assorted scenes along the way. Jay was a sensitive and perceptive guy. Yet, he never said anything, I never said anything and Charlie sure as hell didn't say anything. What's unsaid can be very loud at times and it was becoming intolerable, at least for me. That night I confessed my feelings for Charlie, but not to him: to Jay. I hadn't planned to. It just happened.

After the interview we'd gone to Cafe Noir at Charlie's suggestion. I was only a little surprised to see Danielle and her friend Kate seated in there, eating pitta bread and dips. I wasn't really surprised at all because it seemed that anytime I had a meetup with Charlie, Danielle knew about it and turned up to keep tabs on him – or that was certainly my impression.

This night, like many others, I could see why she might have reason to worry. Charlie was showering me with attention. I was happy to be with him and Jay as I always was, but I was very aware of Danielle's disapproval and also worried that I'd had a bit too much *vin rouge* and I might accidently blurt out something that could be a big mistake. Danielle's friend Kate was friendly and seemed to counteract Danielle's frostiness, but even in my intoxicated state I was aware it might not be sincere. At the same time, in this odd set-up it felt natural to be with Charlie, to be sitting there laughing and joking and grinning at each other as he and Jay sang *Is This Love?* by Bob Marley. He seemed on a real high and I loved him – every inch of him – but the situation was growing increasingly difficult for me. He was now living with Danielle, which normally means things have gotten serious. Yet, that wasn't how it felt but I had to try and sit with the facts.

It became clear after a while that Danielle wanted to go. A taxi arrived and she left, with Kate calling goodbye. Charlie got up to go too. Next thing I knew he was right in my face and giving me a big, affectionate, desirous kiss. I was shocked as I expected Danielle could probably see from outside the big, close by window, but I was also touched. Could this be as hard for him as it was for me? Or was he completely OK with the situation? I truly didn't know.

I still had almost a full glass of wine left so declined another when Jay kindly offered. Jay. He was such a good presence to have around. I was glad he was still there because I felt a wave of anguish wash over me once the others had gone. I knew I was a little drunk, but not drunk enough to shed all inhibitions. Still, I must have been more carefree with my tongue than usual because without pre-planning what was about to fall out of my mouth, it fell out.

"Jay, can I tell you something?"

Jay didn't hesitate. "Please do!" he said, and adopted the posture of a considerate, caring listener. It was out before I knew it. I don't even remember how I phrased it, but it was a confession that I had feelings for Charlie that were beyond friend-type feelings, and some dumb question to Jay about whether Charlie had ever said anything about how he felt about me, which I cringed when I heard myself ask it – but still, I wanted to hear the answer and was prepared for the brutal truth.

Instead I sensed Jay was mildly disappointed that this had been the revelation, and for a split second I wondered if he had been expecting me to confess to feelings for him

– which was not a ridiculous thing for him to assume because I was very fond of Jay, and if it hadn't been for the overpowering connection with Charlie perhaps I would have fallen for him, and this was something that crossed my mind more than once through the years. Jay and I could possibly be good together… if Jay felt that way inclined, which I really didn't know, but at this point, it was all about Charlie and here I was finally confessing my secret to his closest friend.

Jay paused carefully before replying, then said, "I think he feels like we all feel about you", meaning all of the Last Exit Players, I assumed. I didn't even think to ask what that meant, I just took it as the only answer he could give at this point in time and didn't press for any more details. We talked about it a little and Jay said with a sigh, "He seems to have to have this allure with women."

He went on to say he could see why I would find him attractive, knowing how talented he is and having been exposed to his work, and cautiously suggested it was something to do with the pull of him being a moderately successful actor who was becoming slightly famous.

I put him straight there and said, "No, I'd love him whatever he was. It's nothing to do with what he does." I wasn't offended by his suggestion. It was something that I had considered before in the sense that I had almost wished he *wasn't* a little bit famous, wasn't someone who typically attracted admirers, because I was worried it looked like a silly crush, as though it was the actor/film star persona that was the pull. But very early on, I had been sure it wasn't about that. Oh, I was happy for him to be an actor because that's what he was and he *was* hugely talented, but it was the real him that I had fallen for and the more I knew the man inside, with any of the human faults and failings some may say he had, the more I loved him, not less.

"So, you'd love him even if he was a binman." Jay nodded, accepting what I said without question.

"Yeah, definitely," was all I could say. "This is deep."

"Yeah," Jay said kindly, and then gave me a comforting hug. "It's hard, and hard seeing him with someone else."

"Yes, but he seems happy," I found myself saying, and I have no idea why because I didn't really think he was. Why on earth did I say that? Perhaps because I thought it would be impolite to suggest otherwise, and would just make me seem like I was bitching about Danielle.

And perhaps Jay felt he couldn't either because he said, "Er, yeah, though he wasn't... but he seems to be now." I heard the hesitation and sensed it wasn't straightforward but I didn't want to pry and I didn't know how much more I could bear to hear.

We talked for some time and Jay confided a personal issue of his own to me. We promised not to reveal our confessions to anybody. I felt a mild relief I had come clean and that I hadn't been laughed at, but then Jay wasn't the kind of person who would ever do that. We were then joined by Antonio, usually known as Toni, an Italian mutual friend of Jay and Charlie. The conversation switched to other, more mundane things.

I went home that night, even more confused than I'd ever been. I couldn't unravel the truth. Something somewhere wasn't adding up but my tired brain couldn't join up the dots, though it strained to find an explanation, one that explained everything. I only knew my truth, which was try as I might, this love I had for Charlie just didn't feel wrong or in vain. It didn't feel like it should be put away, buried, filed under *doomed*. I felt I had no choice but to live with it for now, to get up each morning and carry on with my life and carry the love in my heart. And I did.

Some nights my pillow would be damp and mascara-smudged, as tears would roll silently in the darkness. Some days I'd feel the sweetest joy when I felt his love, when he gave me those tender and shy smiles, when it felt unmistakeable. There were also days I just felt content and on an even keel, spending time with friends, watching plays, watching bands, strolling in the park – when Charlie wasn't a factor in how good or bad I felt at all. But the truth was that on many days he was a factor, a big factor, too big a factor. Telling Jay changed nothing on the surface but I did somehow feel Jay's support and understanding, even though we never explicitly talked about it again. For that I was very grateful. He was a good friend, a loving soul. Whether he ever told Charlie, even in hints, I don't know.

Nineteen

That preliminary script that Charlie had been so pleased with turned into a full play, which the Last Exit Players performed as part of the Brighton Festival in May the following year. It was wonderful to be working creatively with the group and I think it was no secret to Charlie that some of the subject matter of the play, even though it was a mishmash of things, may have reflected aspects of our situation, though, like a lot of things, it wasn't something we discussed.

The production was called Une Lumière Particulière, and was set in Paris against a backdrop of the events of May 1968. It concerned a student activist who ended up in prison for scrawling graffiti on the wall of the Sorbonne, but also ended up being accused of a murder he didn't commit. His lover campaigned for his freedom and lit a candle for him every evening, symbolising both the eternal flame she carried in her heart for him, and also the idea that the mind can be a prison but that enlightenment – or waking up – can set us free.

The summer of that year was a pivotal time. Despite the buzz of the play being performed and seeing a lot of Charlie in rehearsals where he fleshed out that main, imprisoned character like he had written the play himself, it wasn't the best of times for me and could perhaps be described as a mini dark night of the soul. I'd have a longer and more profound one around three years later. This one was like a warning, a warning that I needed to shift my focus, but I was only dimly aware of how vital that was and how far I had allowed myself to sink into the quicksand. He had a hold on me. The situation had a hold on me. That summer was when I first realised that I had to let go – though letting go completely still seemed utterly impossible. The trigger for realising how much strain I was putting myself under was an illness.

One Saturday morning I woke up with a scratchy throat. I also felt exhausted, which didn't make sense because I'd had a good night's sleep. On top of that I had a low-grade fever of sorts, but nothing too serious, I believed, as it was summer and it was hot. I gulped down some ibuprofen and kept going as normal, though I was conscious that something just didn't feel right.

That night the Last Exit Players were performing the only London performance of Une Lumière Particulière at the King's Head in Islington. Things were a little disjointed within the group and the unity they once shared was starting to fragment. I wanted to support them and I knew some press would be there as well as a photographer friend of mine who was coming down to take some shots, so I felt I needed to be there. Although I felt somewhat ill, it was nothing I couldn't hide. A by-now-familiar kind of night played out. Danielle was strutting about in the pub before the performance, openly glaring at me. Charlie seemed to retreat inside himself and take sanctuary in the dressing room when he wasn't onstage. He and I shared a few pleasant moments where Danielle wasn't breathing down either of our necks, but these moments were becoming more and more fleeting, I was noticing.

When the cast finished performing and the small crowd in the back-room theatre were applauding, I watched in shock as Danielle stormed up to the stage and appeared to be scolding Charlie as the others climbed off the stage into the crowd, as there was no backstage route. Charlie dropped to his feet and fiddled with some technical equipment on the floor, as though to try and hide from the barrage Danielle was throwing at him. I hated to see him being made to feel so small instead of being the glorious soul I knew him to be. I had to look away. I was growing weary of these scenes. They were far too frequent. For whatever reason, I could feel his anguish as well as my own.

Looking back now, I acknowledge I didn't know the full story – their story – and it wasn't my business to know. Perhaps there was a lot more than met the eye. The problem was, I was too caught up in it. I wanted him in my life, otherwise I would have stayed away from situations like this that simply didn't feel good, save a few moments with him, or the moments I could switch off and not allow what was going on to bother me. I sometimes managed this. I sometimes failed. I still, at this point, found it unthinkable to walk away from him. I also felt, on some level, an urge to save him. Perhaps that was rather arrogant of me. Who said he needed saving? At the end of the day, I experienced it as described. He seemed unhappy. She seemed unhappy. I was unhappy. This didn't feel like it was supposed to. It was as though things were becoming increasingly warped and I seemed powerless to do anything about it.

Following the first London performance of the first play I'd written, I didn't want to break down in tears. I didn't want another night that ended that way, but as I walked along Balham High Road after the Tube ride home I could feel those tears building rapidly behind my eyes. There were so many nights that ended uncomfortably, and I'd walk home with toxic energy clinging to my clothes like cigarette smoke that lingered for days. Many of those nights tended to blur into one. Once again, I have to be grateful to Annie for being there on so many of those occasions. She always lent a sympathetic ear and I really appreciated it. Sometimes I would try to keep it in but she tended to know when I was on the brink of tears, and though I hate to admit it, those tears appeared far too often during this particular time.

When I woke in the morning, I dragged myself into the shower feeling awful. My glands were swollen, not just in my neck but I could feel a slight swelling in my armpits. This was enough to concern me. Something was wrong. It was Sunday so I couldn't see a doctor right away, but first thing Monday morning I went down to the local surgery and sat dizzily in the waiting room. I was eventually diagnosed with glandular fever, which I was told was unusual in somebody aged forty. I was relieved to know what was wrong and that though it was unpleasant, I should recover fairly quickly. The thing was, I'd learned enough about healing and the mind-body connection at this stage to recognise that at least some of this was due to the worry and stress I was experiencing regarding Charlie. It was like my body wanted respite from the situation, to switch off, or at the very least to change channels, but day after day I subjected it to the drama of the same questions, the same fears, the same sustained anguish of the same old story. Something had to give.

The glandular fever virus forced me to lie low for a bit. Maybe I needed the seclusion. I was completely alone in the flat because Annie had gone on a trip to the west coast of America with some friends. I wished I could have gone too but I just didn't have the money, and even if I did, I hadn't enough leave left in my annual allowance. Feeling a bit sorry for myself, I lay on the sofa for hours, drifting in and out of sleep. The virus made me feel lousy, spaced-out, semi-delirious at times. Yet part of me was glad to withdraw, to lick my wounds, to just let things lie. I wasn't even thinking of Charlie much at all. For the first time in a long while, I ventured deep inside and let myself just be. And that did actually feel somehow better.

Zharha gave me some good nutritional advice and also sent me lots of energy healing. It wasn't long before the symptoms subsided and I felt more human. The fatigue lingered for a bit, along with some aches and pains in my back, but within a week I was feeling a lot better and returning to my normal routine. I went back to work even though I was still unnaturally tired. My body had to find some way to offload that emotional pain so it's not really surprising I got ill. I wanted to shed this pain, more and more. I wanted to find a solution, to get rid of it, whether that meant being with Charlie or not. I could normally find a solution to most anything but this, this entanglement of my soul with this man's, near defeated me. Yet, I couldn't or wouldn't give up. I felt there was something more that I needed to do, that it wasn't time to walk away. I believed in this love. I believed in his love, even if he hadn't declared it and was living with another woman. It didn't quench the fire. It didn't diminish whatever this thing between us was. I knew in most people's eyes I probably seemed nuts and sometimes wondered if I was too – yet, deep down I knew all this had a reason and the Universe was trying to teach me something. All I could do was trust that this would become apparent one day.

I never told Charlie I'd been ill. I didn't tell him much personal stuff but somehow even a casual conversation between us used to leave me feeling like he could peer right into my soul, and somehow I felt I had the same ability to do this to him. It felt impossible to hide our vulnerabilities from each other and sometimes things spilled out before I'd even realised. I think we both tried to be more cavalier than we truly felt, to try and normalise the interaction, but at the drop of a hat all barriers could dissolve and there was a kind of naked truth between us that was as real as it gets. It was at times like this I knew I could never knowingly hurt him and that he wouldn't hurt me, not intentionally. Just to stop for a moment and realise how rare and wonderful this bond was kept me there, longing for him, dreaming of him, cherishing him even if we weren't 'together'.

Twenty

Charlie's thirtieth birthday was coming up in October of that year. It was events like this that raised my awareness of the age gap between us. Did he have any idea that as he celebrated this new decade, I was already a decade ahead of him? Did it matter? Was it a factor in why he was holding back? Did he think I was too old for him? Somehow I didn't sense he realised the gap was this big. I looked relatively young for my age and my lifestyle was not hugely different than his. Some men prefer older women, some prefer younger, some don't care, I reasoned. The voice in my head warned me that if he wanted children this could be a problem if he didn't get a move on and let me know. But even these nagging voices didn't really concern me, as I didn't feel having children was a priority for him. It wasn't a priority for me and as I'd slid into my forties that summer I realised I was probably not going to have any. There was a tinge of sadness to that realisation, but only maybe in the same way that I also realised I'd probably never visit all the places in the world I'd like to. It had been something I'd wanted in my twenties – or something I *thought* I'd wanted. There'd been two times when I feared I was pregnant and I was terrified, but that was probably more to do with the circumstances not being right.

The older I got the clearer it became to me that there were enough people in the world needing my love, needing to be cared for – adults, older people with no one to look after them, as well as abandoned animals. Bringing more kids on board an overpopulated planet full of people with unmet needs just didn't seem an important thing for me to do in this lifetime.

I'd also expected I'd get married. That hadn't happened either. None of my previous relationships had gone down particularly traditional routes. I had no regrets about this. Marriage wasn't a big deal to me… but love most certainly was. When I looked at Charlie I just didn't feel any discrepancy between us – age didn't matter, money didn't matter, social standing didn't matter, looks didn't matter (though I fancied him like crazy). On a deep level I knew that even if he somehow lost his looks or health or talent or whatever the outer trappings of attraction are, it wouldn't change the way I loved him. I just loved him. I felt no need to marry him or have children but would be equally happy to if that was what came to happen. I just wanted to share my life with him.

Here I was putting the cart before the horse yet again. At this moment in time he was in a relationship with somebody else. I was forty and he was about to become thirty. It was time to wrap up this inner monologue. Yet, these endless preambles and ponderings kept on running round my brain like a hamster on a wheel, chasing round and round instead of leaping off. Anything could happen and nothing could happen. I really ought not to be waiting round to see.

He asked me to come to his birthday party several

times, as though it was important to him that I was there. Of course, I wanted to be there but I also knew it wouldn't be an easy night. It wasn't. Danielle was in overdrive from the minute Annie and I stepped in the door of Cafe Noir. As soon as I perched at the bar with Annie, Danielle speedily perched herself nearby, talking loudly and working hard on giving the impression she was having a good time. The over-the-top antics had begun again. I wasn't too bothered about them. I was used to her behaviour by now and she wasn't fooling me, which I think she knew. You can't pull the wool over the eyes of the soul... though you can do a damn good job at bewildering it and challenging someone to trust their soul insights rather than the screeching voice of the ego.

When Charlie appeared, naturally, I had to go and wish him happy birthday and give him his gift (a bottle of good-quality, unusual bourbon I'd found in a new, quirky off-licence that had opened in Balham). He opened his arms to hug and thank me, but as we fell into an embrace I was suddenly elbowed out of the way by Danielle, who literally pulled him away from me and pushed him into a sitting position on one of the Cafe Noir armchairs. She then sat down on the arm of the chair beside him, stroking his face, while Charlie kind of gasped his thanks to me. I nodded that it was OK and stepped aside. I didn't go near him for the rest of the night and he didn't go near me. What was the point? It was uncomfortable but I wasn't interested in playing games. Annie and I stayed for a while – for as long as was polite – but the atmosphere was edgy and after a couple of hours we got out of there.

It was hard not to feel upset but it was the sort of

night I had expected for some reason. There seemed nothing I could really do and I knew I should probably just stay away. It all hurt too much, but it seemed so hard to extricate myself from the dumb drama I'd got myself involved in.

When I finally fell into troubled dreams that night I found myself lying at the foot of the stairs leading down to the toilets in Cafe Noir. I was dreaming, yet on some level I actually felt I was on location in real time, as the place was now empty and shut up and the only sound was the whirr of refrigerators. I lay in a crumpled heap at the foot of the stairs and I seemed to have lost my ability to walk. I knew it was a temporary state, but it was a temporary state that left me helpless and I sobbed. Next thing I knew, arms were reaching down towards me and I was being hoisted up. It was Charlie. He gathered me into his arms and slowly and carefully carried me up the stairs from the basement to ground level. We didn't speak. We didn't need to. I felt everything he wanted to say, which was *I'm sorry and it won't always be like this, and I love you.* I can still see us at the top of the stairs in the empty bar with the orange light from the street lamps streaking the tabletops and the eerie hum of the electrics vibrating around us in the dead of the night.

I woke feeling acute sorrow. I knew he loved me and of course that was wonderful, but the love felt tragic, like we were caught in a trap, a fairy tale gone wrong or at least stuck in a dark place. Somewhere deep down, I knew that most fairy tales had happy endings, but they also had fearsome disturbances in the middle. At the same time, I also knew that to envision Charlie as a knight in shining armour wasn't a good idea and this *wasn't* a fairy tale. On so many levels I felt it was *my* duty to save *him*. But how to do that? And what from exactly?

I found it hard not to reach out to him if much time went by without contact, and usually not much time did. If we hadn't had contact for a month or so I'd usually find a reason to call – or sometimes, less frequently, he would. I don't remember what my reason was but one afternoon when that gap felt too long and too wide I remember pressing the call button on my mobile and being stunned at his response when he picked up.

"Eileen, Eileen, Eileen, Eileen, *Eileen!*" he exclaimed with what sounded like pure joy. It was as though he thought he'd never hear from me again. I had no idea what had caused his delight in receiving this call but the delight, almost relief, was unmistakable. It was things like this that I reminded myself of occasionally when I got bogged down in doubt, questioning his feelings. Did he realise how he sounded? Did he want me to know he missed me like I missed him? *Did* he miss me like I missed him? I just couldn't figure it out and trying to only resulted in getting me tied up in tighter and more uncomfortable knots.

Good, bad and mediocre days followed and nothing seemed to change in any definitive way. I still saw Charlie reasonably regularly and we still had some lovely little episodes, magic moments that glittered like pearls on a rocky terrain, beautiful moments that soothed my soul, like dipping tired feet into cooling rock pools and recognising those pearls that were shimmering below the surface. Little did I know at this point, those metaphorical rock pools were freely available and weren't dependent on

Charlie's presence – but his presence had the power to take me there quicker than any drug or dream I knew. No matter how I looked at it, life seemed so much better with him in it than without him, even in small snatches, even when he was with another. I just didn't want to lose him.

I remember an encounter one night when Charlie's friend Louis was playing records at a venue in Shoreditch. He was full of warmth and tenderness. He appeared behind me at the bar and winked.

"So what song would you like to hear, then?"

I couldn't think off the top of my head, so I said, "Surprise me" as I navigated my way back to the table I was sitting at with Annie. I watched him return to Louis with two pints of lager and a short discussion ensued. Charlie then began rooting through Louis' record bags. My soul jumped with delight when a few minutes later he played a song that had inhabited my head all day – and days before. It was a soft, trippy but determined track called *Sunshine Superman* by Donovan where the singer tells his beloved that though it would take time, he would make her his own and would do so in style.

I was quite shocked that he seemed to have plucked that song out of the cosmos. It was impossible not to get the message, to see it as a sign. Perhaps it was moments like this that kept me hanging on to hope. He gave me too many signals that there was something to hope for. But how long can you wait? And can you read too much into signs, even when you get so many you're tripping over them?

Zharha still assured me *it* would happen, though she also told me I had to let go, and I had to keep living my life and I couldn't just keep waiting. I agreed, and though I attempted to let go, I don't think at this point I had dropped the rope. I had loosened my grip but I was still looking over my shoulder way too much, waiting for him to show up, waiting for him to call. I knew it wasn't healthy but that pull was so strong. I beat myself up about my seeming inability to forget about him. I worried there was something wrong with me. I could put my thoughts of him aside for short periods, but before long they'd intrude on whatever I was doing, wherever I was.

I'd had this problem to some degree before with other loves in the past but none that persisted this long, and there was something different about the way Charlie filled my head. It wasn't simply that I'd think of him, it was like he was actually there, in my head – his energy, his spirit, his thoughts and feelings seemed to permeate my own and they'd get mixed up together, shaken and stirred like a swirling cocktail of confusion. The space between us seemed nebulous, there weren't the same boundaries that seemed to be in place with other people and it felt as though our energies were leaking into each other's fields. He simply seemed to be with me, non-physically, and I could only wonder if I was non-physically hanging out with him too. Maybe he experienced it the same way, maybe he didn't. Maybe I was going crazy, maybe I wasn't. Maybe answers would come soon... maybe they wouldn't. There was simply no way of knowing – and needing to know was one of the things I had to drop, to surrender to the sea of unknowingness and trust that I would float whatever the outcome, whatever the weather, whether or never... that surrender was the only way to shut up the jabbering questions of my ego.

Twenty-One

In the first few months of the following year I made a decision. I was going to tell Charlie how I felt – not about all the strange and fated feelings specifically, not about my pain or my dreams or the way he'd somehow cracked open my entire being, not about how downright weird my life had become since he'd been a part of it, but just that I loved him. I'd never wanted it to be this way, to tell him whilst he was in a relationship with someone else, but I needed to do it for myself. I'd been stuck not knowing what to do for so long. If I didn't believe he had feelings for me I wouldn't have dreamt of stepping up and saying my piece. I needed to break the pattern somehow and this would surely liberate me one way or another. If it was all out in the open perhaps a change of direction could come about. I could hopefully move on, knowing where I stood with him. So, I discussed it with Zharha and with Annie. We all agreed it was time to do *something*.

I made sure I knew I could live with the consequences of my actions. I was clear that I would do it in as discreet a way as possible and in such a way that put no pressure on him. I just wanted him to know, to know for sure, because even though I suspected he knew how I felt, in the same way I suspected I knew how *he* felt, I knew how much I second-guessed myself and talked myself out of things – even things that seemed incredibly obvious. This way he could know it wasn't in his head and hopefully I could find some kind of peace by being honest about the situation.

My stipulation with this admission was that it had to be in person. I didn't want to do it over the phone, or by email or in a letter – it had to be woman to man, heart to heart, soul to soul. We also had to be alone. This seemed only fair to both of us. I didn't want to embarrass him. I didn't want it to be uncomfortable, though I knew some discomfort was inevitable. I wanted him to know I was serious, but that I was being mature and realistic about it. I scribbled down words I might use, phrases I might dress this in. I scrubbed them out again. Most of what came to mind sounded either cheesy or weird or clichéd. Still, I didn't take too long to find a few sentences that I thought I could actually say. It would be short, and to the point. Once I knew what I wanted to say, I said it out loud to myself a few times and despite the inward cringing, I got to a place where I felt I could say this to Charlie. Indeed, I *had* to say this to Charlie.

So now, it was a waiting game, searching for that window of opportunity where this revelation could happen. After a couple of weeks I realised this window was proving to be frustratingly elusive. I was bumping into him often enough, but the situation was never right. There were too many people barging about, or the mood was wrong. I knew that Danielle being anywhere in the vicinity was a giant, flapping red flag. Timing had seemed orchestrated beyond our control from the start and I knew it would present an opportunity sooner or later.

Strangely enough, as soon as I made the internal decision to tell Charlie, he phoned me several times about inconsequential things, as though unconsciously he had picked up the fact that I had something important to say. It was always good to hear his voice on the phone so this was a bonus, but I was determined not to make my confession via that medium – or even to set up a meeting in that way. It didn't feel right, and for my own sake, I wanted to see his eyes, I wanted see his body language – not that I was telling him to try and suss out his feelings specifically, though of course I wanted to know how he truly felt, but I was clear in my mind that this was primarily an attempt to unlock myself, to move forward, to break the limbo. Once I knew he was aware, then I no longer had to wonder if he knew, and no longer had to hide, or hold everything inside, at least where he was concerned. I knew it may be that we never discussed it again, but at least on some level the dam could be released, the inertia might end. I just wanted to be honest with myself and his self, with our selves.

It took around six weeks between making the decision to spill the beans and doing the deed. Sitting on it had been agonising but finally I found my way to set free those strings of words describing the big love that had been inhabiting and firing my heart for so long. Charlie had phoned me to say a band we both liked, and that Jay had created a record sleeve for, were playing in Hudson's Cave and to come down if I could. I decided tonight was the night, as long as I could get him on his own. It was going to have to be a direct approach involving asking him to step outside, perhaps up the graffiti-splattered stairway that led onto a flat roof above the bar. If I could subtly ask him to do this we could hopefully have a private moment. I didn't do anything different with my make-up or my clothes. This was not an attempt to seduce or elicit a response. I wanted to be the real me, like I'd always been with him. This was all about being real and making a long-term situation that had loomed in my head into a concrete confession, to expand the walls so it was no longer confined to those inner chambers and could breathe out in the open. What happened after that was in the lap of the gods.

I entered the realm of Hudson's Cave on that Sunday evening. The band were due onstage around ten and the Cave jukebox was blaring out an interesting playlist. Usually at pivotal moments in my life, if there's music playing, the record cements the scene in my mind but I couldn't tell you what record happened to be playing when I made my move. I'd sat with Annie for just over an hour beforehand, trying to be as normal as possible. I made sure I didn't have more than one drink, which I sipped as slowly as was humanly possible. This couldn't be a drunken expression. I needed to be at least almost fully sober. Even though I was terrified, I had no intention of pulling out.

I didn't interact with Charlie much during the evening and my main memory is that he was loudly discussing plans for a house-warming party, as he and Danielle had bought a new flat. I'd already known about that and I guess some would say they were obviously contemplating a long-term future by doing something like this. I would agree, and perhaps that was partly why I felt the need to get this off my chest and move on. I assumed moving on was possible. I assumed that it would be easier after clearing the air, laying my heart on the line, and making it easy for him, if he did share my feelings, to reciprocate. There'd be no more speculation after this, I told myself. *I'll know where I stand.*

Danielle wasn't around that night. If she had been I wouldn't have done what I was about to do. Somehow when it came to it, adrenaline propelled me forward and I swallowed my fear and approached him calmly and as discreetly as can be done in a public place. There was nobody else too close by.

His big, beautiful blue eyes looked surprised when I was suddenly standing before him saying, "Can I have a word? In private?" He didn't hesitate, though he did ask if he could visit the toilet before, which he did, and I waited by the bar, trying to appear completely casual, peering at some artwork that hung near the bar as though I'd never noticed it before, even though I knew it inside out. I knew every nook and cranny of the Cave inside out. When Charlie returned we stepped through a door that led to the alley running alongside the railway bridge, and instinctively we both headed up the stairs to the roof. There we were, alone at last, under a starry sky.

"What's wrong?" Charlie asked with outstretched arms.

I don't remember the sequence of my words but their content was as intended, and I made sure to state at the beginning that I wasn't asking anything of him and that he didn't need to say anything if he didn't want to. The lines tumbled out. The barrier crumbled. Phrases like "feelings more than friendship", "this isn't some silly crush", "have felt this way for a long time" and "I love you" landed at the door of his heart.

That door was at least halfway open because shortly after my speech he opened his arms and said, "Come here" and hugged me close. I barely registered what was happening or how it felt to be in his arms. For a short time I stood there, wrapped in his embrace with my face against his heart. It felt like where I belonged, but sadly I knew I couldn't linger there and it was me that broke the hug and stepped back. Even though I'd told him he didn't have to say anything, he said a lot of things, only some of which I remember.

He said, "but we've always got on so well", "I think the world of you!", "but I'm in a relationship" and "I don't know what I can offer you." He sounded agonised, searching, attempting to digest what I'd just thrown in his lap. I'd already expected that he wasn't going to tell me he felt the same way there and then, even if he did – but I was surprised when he said, with his head hanging and not looking me in the eye, "I'm happy with Danielle."

I fell silent and didn't respond. I didn't believe him but I wasn't going to argue. I wasn't asking him to be with me, to leave her or tell me he loved me. I was grateful that he'd listened. I could tell he had taken it seriously.

He kept talking, perhaps because he felt panic. He said, "I'll tell you what, though, if you need a friend, I'll be the best friend you could ever have." That was a beautiful thing to say, but once again I didn't fully take it in right there and then.

"Would you rather I hadn't told you?" I asked him.

He said, again sounding in turmoil, "I don't know!"

I said I thought it was better out than in. He didn't know.

We'd probably been immersed in this conversation for five to ten minutes by time I felt the urge to scoot. I'd said my piece and though Charlie seemed to be still turning things over – almost searching for some kind of resolution – I knew it was time to go. The band were tuning up downstairs and I just needed to get out, to attempt to consolidate my soul, to make sure I was still in one piece after the avalanche of words I'd just caused to collapse around us both. I don't remember how I phrased it but I told him I had to leave. I climbed gingerly back down the stairs and floated unseeingly through the bar. Once out on the street I just kept moving and walked home, strangely with no tears in my eyes, resisting the desire to look over my shoulder despite the almighty pull I felt behind me. There was a sense I'd left him in discomfort if not downright brutal pain, and that was never my intention. Why I felt that, I don't exactly know. Did he just feel empathy for my pain? Did I make him feel bad in some way?

I wasn't sure if it had gone as I planned as I wasn't sure what I had expected. The important thing seemed to be that I had done it. It was out in the open and there was no going back. For evermore, he'd have this knowledge, whether he wanted it or not. For evermore, my cards were now on the table for him to see. I did experience some relief and for that I was grateful, but even though the intention had been to release it so I could move on I actually felt as convinced as ever that there was at least a medium-sized portion of mutuality of feeling here, which made me feel that there was a point to hanging on. I had to take him at his word, but his statement about being happy with Danielle just didn't ring true. I could accept that he may not be especially *unhappy*, that it may even have been a comfortable arrangement, a convenient set-up for him for whatever reason – that there may be aspects of the situation he was happy with – but I just couldn't fall for his declaration of being in a happy relationship – or not a happy relationship as I understood those words. But if this was the line he wanted to give me I had no intention of challenging it. I respected what he'd said, and I knew it was still possible I had somehow been mistaken regarding his true feelings. He wanted me to hear he was happy and that he was unavailable so he delivered those lines and I heard them – but the empty feeling they carried just fell away on the night air, almost as though he was trying to convince himself more than me, as if he knew I knew anyway but had to attempt some kind of meaningless disguise.

Regardless of how the land truly lay, I knew I had to carry on walking on it, hobbling over its hills or sliding down its glades – real or imagined, I would carry on. I felt stronger than I imagined I might after my big confession. Perhaps it was just the liberation of no longer having to wrap my heart up and gag my mouth. It might never be mentioned again, and at least for now, I didn't expect it would. But something had shifted energetically and even though it was a little scary, I welcomed the new feeling.

It was late when I got home and I told Annie the gist of what had happened. A few tears were shed, yet I didn't feel in pieces. Annie was as unconvinced as me about Charlie's mention of happiness but we both agreed he'd been taken off guard and all kinds of things can spew from our mouths when that happens. Next morning I got in touch with Zharha and filled her in.

"Oh, he is such a *liar*! Liar, liar, pants on fire… that man is *not* happy in that relationship. You know it, I know it, *she* knows it, he knows it, his friends know it! It's like he is a member of a cult or something," Zharha exclaimed. "*Wow*! That is what I key in on, because you *know* he has feelings and his stomach was doing flip-flops the whole time you were speaking! Like, yippee! Oh, what an ass! Sorry, I am just really pissed now that the guy won't make any move… He should have grabbed you and kissed you immediately."

It was a comfort to get Zharha's straight-talking, passionate response. Much as I would have liked the 'grab and kiss me' scenario too I felt strangely OK with how it had gone. Charlie was in a relationship, happy or unhappy. I'd much rather he untangled himself before coming to me, if he had any intention of doing that. Also, he had made it clear he cared. I had no doubt our friendship – or whatever category in which you'd place what we were to each other – meant something important to him.

Twenty-Two

Oh, the skies! Skies speak to us sometimes in a way words never will. It's that silent enormity of mood and texture interwoven with certain kinds of light. For some reason, in the days following my confession the normal blue and fluffy skies of May became dark and brooding. A few evenings after the fated night, I stood waiting for a bus in Brixton. Clouds were flocking together fast, knitting themselves into a potent, inky canvas that grew heavier with each passing wrong-numbered bus. This pregnant sky perfectly matched the feeling hanging between Charlie and myself. I vividly recall looking out over the high-rise blocks of Brixton, at the vacant billboards opposite waiting to be splashed with smug, deluding advertising, listening to the heartbeat of the city pounding under those strained skies, wondering where Charlie was, wondering about his thoughts, his feelings, his plans, his dreams... did they include me the way mine nestled around him? Somehow, I could feel him... it was a tense kind of torment. I traced a feeling of elation followed by a sinking feeling of entrapment. I also felt he wanted to say something more to me about this. Whether I was picking up anything accurately was hard to say, but I certainly didn't feel he'd taken this lightly or indifferently and that was a good thing.

During this time, there were various discussions and possibilities going on with my play. There was even a film-maker who was interested in reworking it as a screenplay. Whenever I had dealings with the Last Exit Players it tended to be Charlie that I spoke to. The film-maker had some specific questions which I felt Charlie needed to be involved with but I was worried about contacting him after the confession. I told myself I had nothing to fear. My intention was to carry on as normal, not as though I hadn't said what I said, as I meant every word, but I told myself there was no reason why we shouldn't be speaking, or should avoid each other. So I called him, discovering that he had tried to contact me too by email but for some reason I hadn't received his message.

A flurry of phone calls and texts occurred over the next few weeks, all with an official business subject line but I think below the surface we were both processing what had happened. For whatever reason, he seemed very keen to work with me. He seemed to be coming up with some great ideas too and there was a fantastic, shining energy between us. He had a particular idea he wanted us to go and talk to Hudson about and told me to meet him outside the Cave one evening before it opened so we could run through it ourselves first.

I remember turning up and Hudson crashing in on us, so we never had that alone time. We rarely did these days. Consciously or unconsciously, Hudson seemed to dampen things. He didn't want to take our ideas on board. Charlie and I were both disappointed but we accepted it without much discussion. Somehow, things fell into a lull between us and I didn't see much of him for several weeks.

During this time I had some long talks with Zharha, who told me I had to let go. She was still sure things would work out between us eventually but for my own sake I had to let go. I still found the idea difficult to contemplate, but I could see the wisdom in it. So, I made an effort to turn my attention elsewhere. Some days I did very well. Some days I literally pined for his presence. I kept trying, however, to keep on an even keel. I knew on some deep level that things weren't over, whatever that means, but I worried about how to keep him in my life, feeling it was important to do that, not trusting if it was meant to be that it would just be. He just seemed too precious to lose and when I didn't see much of him I worried, then scolded myself for it. Looking back now my fears seem faintly ridiculous, this need I had to see him in case he forgot me. If he was going to forget me, he would forget me. I wasn't forgetting *him* by not seeing him – quite the opposite – so it could be the same for him. After all, this was, as I was beginning to understand, a connection of souls and physical bodies were only part of the deal. This was something I needed to learn, not just about Charlie and me and our unusual connection, but about what I was doing on this planet in the first place, what it was all about.

I hadn't fully grasped the knowing I now have, that we are souls (or non-physical beings) first and foremost, residing (mostly) in physical bodies and our three-dimensional mentality can blind us to this fact very easily. I also had a nagging impulse that I had to be doing something all the time to help this love along. I had a problem with letting it be. Even though it was the surest, strongest, biggest love I'd ever felt for a man, or maybe *because* it was, I somehow doubted its ability to fully manifest, as though something this good just couldn't be possible. Perhaps it was because it felt so precious that I felt the need to cling to it so tightly in my mind. I mean, I didn't even have him by my side, but that was just it… this love didn't need to be my side. It was everywhere, but at this point I still held on to Charlie as being that source, the vessel from which that dazzling feeling flowed. I wasn't wrong that Charlie was the vessel, but I was wrong to see him as the only gateway. He just happened to be the quickest, most powerful activator of that kind of bliss I had ever known, but I didn't fully comprehend this at this particular moment. Flashes of panic hit me when I thought he might slip away – this beautiful dream I had built (or we had built?), it couldn't all be for nothing, could it? At the end of the day it certainly wasn't all for nothing because I was learning valuable lessons but I needed to be whacked over the head a few more times before I got it, digested it and took it on board. No other person can ever be the gateway to happiness. The gatekeeper to happiness was me.

Zharha warned me that I was in danger of losing myself if I continued to focus too much on Charlie. I could see this was a danger so I attempted to bring focus back to myself and my own life, yet it was so easy for my thoughts to encircle their threads around him, neglecting to give myself the same attention. Why was this so damned hard? Why did he sit in my head so much? That pull that had been there from the start was still there, like a cord that tugged at my heart, and the further I got away from him, sometimes the more it yanked me back, like some kind of terror that if I walked too far away I would lose him. I don't know why I felt this strange magnetic pull. It was almost as though he was a part of me, and in a very real way to force him out of my heart and headspace seemed as though I was attempting to cut off an arm or leg in an effort to set myself free. Despite my confession and that hope of liberation I was still intrinsically attached to him. He was still so dear to me. I literally couldn't forget him for any decent length of time. I was starting to worry that there really *was* something wrong with me, yet I also felt how wonderful this love was and that there was a real gift tied in with all gut-wrenching heartache. What could be wrong with love? Nothing, of course. But what was making me suffer wasn't love – it was need; it was desire. That was where the problem lay, but at this point I wasn't seeing the vast difference between love and need.

I remember my birthday that year. It was a relatively warm June evening. Summers hadn't been what they used to be in recent years but on this night, as the sun started to slip down below the horizon its heat stayed wrapped around the streets and I felt a strange familiar nostalgia as I arrived at Hudson's Cave with Annie. Charlie was outside with a guy I didn't know. He was pulling on a cigarette with that vaguely devilish but lovable smile curling his lips.

"Ah, it's the birthday girl." He winked. It was good to see him as lately we didn't see each other quite as much as we used to.

Once inside and when I was alone he said, "How old you are you today, then?" followed by, in almost the same breath, "Or is it rude to ask?" I took the easy way out and told him it was, even though I didn't actually think it was rude. He had every right to know how old I was and that I was a decade older than him, but perhaps I felt too vulnerable to reveal that at that specific moment. Besides, Hudson had dragged it out of me and all Charlie would have to do was ask him if he really wanted to know, and I expect he probably did.

Several of my friends were around that evening to raise a glass. I enjoyed the night and distracted myself from Charlie as much as possible. It wasn't too hard when I had good company but I did steal glances at him from time to time. Charlie's friend, Louis, was DJ again and played some good tunes as he always did. A mixture of the summer heat and alcohol fuelled a spree of dancing. Only the women got up and danced – on the stage, on the floor, wherever there was space. I remember as one record ended and I turned to get off the stage and resume my drinking, I caught Charlie watching me. He looked like a naughty schoolboy who'd been caught trying to catch a glimpse through a crack in the door of the girls' changing room. I smiled. He smiled with a kind of relief and got back to his position with the boys. I can still see that moment because there was no mistaking it. It was the look of love. Yes, there was lust thrown in, which is perfectly OK. On some level my soul photographed that look on his face because I can still see it, and because it said more than words can or ever will. After all this time, those unspoken feelings were still speaking.

The night went on and though I don't tend to drink to excess too often, that particular night the table held a line of drinks people had bought me and it felt impolite not to at least attempt to knock some back. Still, even alcohol couldn't shut out the feeling emitting from Charlie, which only seemed to intensify as the night went on. He seemed sad, a little withdrawn. I felt him watching shyly on and off but we didn't talk much at all that night. I guessed it was probably difficult because I was surrounded by my mates, who were all decidedly tipsy. I wished I wasn't so aware of him but the fact is, I was, though I tried not to let it look that way. On some level I felt we needed a good chat. Did we need to revisit the confession on the roof? I wasn't sure it was a good idea unless he wanted to. If he had something to say it was up to him to say it, wasn't it? Anyone could see the ball was in his court, surely? Yet, I could feel it was incredibly difficult for him to come to me and I didn't quite know why that was. As far as I knew he was still with Danielle so I assumed he felt he couldn't while that was still the case, and perhaps he didn't *want* to get closer. Perhaps he was happy to just to be friends. Yet, we weren't really that at the moment either. That birthday night had felt awkward in a new way, and I didn't want us to feel awkward. The air felt like it needed to be cleared; yet I didn't feel I could clear it as I didn't know what was causing the emotional smog that was creeping in. I guessed it was a repercussion of my confession, even though that had been several months ago now and I hadn't sensed it before.

Next morning, as I didn't have to go the office, I pottered around the flat, drinking tea and replaying scenes from the previous evening. I was aware Charlie had missed the last train home to Streatham Hill as the night had gone on a little beyond closing time, and I felt vaguely responsible for that, which was kind of ridiculous as no one was forcing him to stay, though I think he dutifully wanted to help Louis get all his stuff home. It was good of him to stay and it was nice of him to come in the first place.

With a sudden impulse of gratitude and affection I picked up the phone and called him before even thinking about it. Usually I thought long and hard before calling him, always having to take a deep breath or two before dialling his number. He answered immediately and spoke softly. There was nothing special to say but I wanted him to know I appreciated him being there and told him we'd all had a good time. He said he was glad and seemed very gentle, but once again I detected that sadness I'd felt from him during the evening before. It was hard to put my finger on it but something felt different, as though he was somehow bowing out, resigning. I couldn't really make sense of it but it worried me a little. He was at work so we didn't talk for long. He'd recently started working for the council. I wasn't sure exactly what he was doing but I knew it was because he needed the money. I put down the phone, feeling a pang of anguish as well as a warm wave of love. I just wanted to throw my arms around him, comfort him, drown him in sweet love and see him smile, but he seemed miles away, and as though he were moving further and further out of reach.

Next time I saw him, around a week later, only confirmed the presence of an increasing void. It was in Hudson's Cave, as so many of our encounters were. Danielle appeared to be on a mission to prove her ownership, literally frogmarching him about the Cave.

My heart sank to see it but I had no desire to compete. What I felt for Charlie was made of pure tenderness and words like 'ownership' or 'competition' just didn't enter that space. This wasn't easy for any of us – not for Charlie, not for Danielle and not for me. I had a strong sense that the situation had come into being for *all* of us to learn something. There had to be a bigger plan at work. He and Danielle were together for a reason. Maybe she could teach him things and show him things I couldn't. My job was to learn my lessons and let them get on with their stuff. Charlie shot me a few looks that night which I interpreted (rightly or wrongly) as, *Sorry about this, but what can I do? I've got no choice but to go along with it.*

I did find this somewhat irritating but as he didn't verbalise his case and I was basing his attitude upon a few shrugs and facial expressions there was nothing I could say.

The way I saw it, he did have a choice. Then again, so did I. I had a choice about how to respond, whether to let this upset me or whether to rise above it – to see it as a kick in the teeth or an opportunity for growth.

In hindsight, part of me wishes I'd just backed off completely at this point, just given up and walked away – but once again my heart just wouldn't let me.

It was both the love he'd sparked in me and the huge feeling of destiny that had surrounded our bond from the start that kept me plugged in. When it feels like angels have dragged and placed paving stones engraved with your name and his in front of you, beckoning you to walk along them, it's very hard to find those paving stones aren't leading where you thought they would, and in fact the path is looking like it's about to fork off in different directions. It's also been strewn with all kinds of debris, roadblocks, traffic lights that seem stuck on red – yet, I still felt those original magic paving stones under my bare toes when I kicked off my everyday shoes and listened in stillness. When I tuned into my heart, I still heard Gabriel's jubilant horn, telling me, *This is it! This is for you-hoo!* So, what do you do? I couldn't stop loving but I started sadly taking a step or two back. We'd begun our long, slow goodbye.

Twenty-Three

Did I fail to consciously recognise it? Could I not bear to admit it? I'm not entirely sure but whether I wanted to admit it or not, it was becoming clear that Charlie was backing off. At the same time I was edging away too, but I suspect our retreats were not for the same reason. It was a gradual retreat so for a while we still saw each other from time to time, once a month perhaps, and sometimes it was still pleasant enough. Yet, the tension that had crept in after my birthday had quietly taken root. Something was different. I wondered if he'd decided he *had* to cut off from me to save himself the hassle of Danielle getting upset, or to save himself dealing with the feelings our connection triggered – or could it be he thought it was unhealthy for me to keep seeing him if he had decided nothing could ever happen between us? Had he decided that? I really didn't know. It could be a mixture of all those things – or even none of them.

It wasn't hard to see why Danielle was bothered by me when I looked at Charlie looking at me. Even now, at times he would just stare at me like he literally couldn't help it and I know I must have stared back at him just as helplessly. How could she *not* know – or at least strongly suspect – there was something between us, something deep, something that wasn't as simple as mere physical attraction or even a meeting of minds? It was perhaps the unusualness of the bond that was so perplexing and compelling. I knew for me it was like nothing I'd known before, I suspected the same for him, and even for others who witnessed it, it was a puzzle. I'd felt this often. Something that could be sensed a mile off energetically, yet the source of this energy was mysterious and people had trouble articulating or discerning what it was and where it came from. It took me a while to really take that on board but eventually, it was the only thing that could explain the odd things that happened around us, the odd things that people said or reactions they had. I came to just accept it even if I didn't understand it.

Whatever the reasons, Charlie became more withdrawn with me – though after a while I sensed he was withdrawing with everyone, to some extent. Perhaps it wasn't as personal as it felt but I couldn't, at that time, see it any other way. Although things weren't quite the same superficially, the intensity around us when we did meet hadn't diminished. It was just being held in check by both of us, like a cumbersome time bomb ticking loudly in a corner. It was very awkward to conceal. Neither of us had asked for it or were consciously responsible for setting it and neither us wanted to ignite it, yet, and I think I speak for both of us here, neither of us could ignore it and if we could only find a way to detonate it safely so that no one was harmed in the process and to use that startling energy productively, we surely would. It was the kind of energy that could change the world, but that's a very scary energy to deal with sometimes.

Yet, the truth is, there was nothing dangerous about

this other than the likelihood that energy like that will inflame every shadow that lurks inside you, fears you never knew you had: the fear that if you find something this precious you might lose it, the fear that if you truly give your heart you can never take it back. And it's true, you can't. But it's learning that love doesn't have to hurt and if your heart grows big enough (and it will if you let it), you won't feel any loss because the love is everlasting, a state of being rather than something you possess.

Part of me knew that this love and this situation were worth taking risks for. To push them away never felt right. To deny my feelings never felt right. One of the positive things that had happened since meeting Charlie had been my commitment to facing my fears. I now looked them squarely in the eye, and looked at myself squarely in the eye. I was aware that he somehow pushed me to be honest with myself and to find my strength, even when it felt like I didn't have any left. It was an endless trawl into the trenches of my soul and over time, I built and filled those inner reservoirs. There was help, some from earthly beings, some from the mysterious Universe that seemed determined I would rise to the challenge, but nothing worked without me pulling up my sleeves and getting stuck in, digging those foundations and not losing sight of the fact that I was the architect and if I wanted a beautiful world I had to consciously create it, and not get put off by the mud, sweat and chaos involved in making something beautiful – and not get diverted or led astray by the noise and commotion of the ego. All in all this was an extremely positive journey; it just looked a bit of mess when viewed in sorry, shaky snapshots without the bigger picture, without the soul's wise and patient pathways being considered.

It was around this time that Charlie stopped answering my calls, or rather, he answered more sporadically for a while. This hurt me. I didn't call often and I generally only called with a specific purpose, usually to do with the Last Exit Players or my journalism. On several occasions he didn't pick up the phone or call back and this is when I knew he really was backing off. I still had a good relationship with Jay and he kept me up to date on the drama group stuff and let me know what was happening. He also acknowledged that Charlie was being difficult and seemed to feel a need to apologise or even compensate at times. This was very sweet of him and I was touched by his consideration. Though part of me wanted to quiz Jay on what the hell was *really* going on with Charlie, I refrained. It wasn't my place to poke and it wasn't fair on Jay.

I put on a brave face and tried my best not to take it too personally. I knew I hadn't done anything to offend him – or nothing I was aware of. I couldn't even speculate as to why he backed off because I just didn't know what was going on in his life or his head or his heart. Perhaps he really thought it was easier for me as well as him to just cut ties; maybe he was being considerate, seeing as he couldn't offer me anything, as he'd put it – though he had offered me something: to be the best friend I could ever have. There was the apparent contradiction. I couldn't get those words out of my head, and I knew he had meant them at the time. I tried to reason it away but nothing really made sense other than either his feelings towards me had changed or he'd just decided it was best to keep a distance because of the intensity, because he was in a relationship and didn't want to hurt Danielle, because our connection freaked him out, because it all felt too much. Maybe he *was* doing me a favour. Maybe I should do the same.

So, I continued to turn my focus back to myself and my life. Since this whole journey had been happening I had become far more sensitive to energy, or perhaps I always had been, but I was more aware of the energy of people and places – and more aware of its effect on me. It was becoming clearer to me also that I was highly empathic, soaking up emotion and discord, as well as more positive vibrations, like a sponge. I was learning that I needed to handle all this better than I was. I needed to heal what was mine and release what wasn't. I took various classes on healing over the next few years and the more I learned, the more I marvelled at the intricacies of energy fields, of the connection between body and mind. There really was more to life than met the eye superficially. It really wasn't difficult to enter these alternative realms, where all kinds of magic could happen.

One thing that really did stay with me was my experience with a plant. Most of us have heard people say that lovingly talking to plants enhances their growth and well-being but I discovered that maybe that they can talk to us too, and that floored me. I was doing a healing course in a rambling farmhouse on a hill somewhere in the Sussex countryside. It was a magical few days with a soulful group of people and I was starting to feel I belonged in this field, though I was still a bit wary of New Age nonsense and people who pulled angel cards every five minutes, but overall I was being led onto a spiritual path. However, I wasn't embracing it one hundred per cent; some part was hanging back. Perhaps I saw it as a path away from Charlie. Perhaps I was worried if I walked too far down it I'd lose sight of him and he'd lose sight of me. Zharha had made that suggestion and there was some truth in it. Yet, I also felt there were a lot of charlatans out there and I didn't want to be misinformed, led astray or brainwashed. Still, I understood that you had to come with an open heart. It was wise to question and it was wise to trust your instincts, but it was important to be open. I was open. I may have had a few blocks but I had an open nature and a trusting heart and I sincerely wanted to help heal the world, as well as myself.

So that weekend, the teachers on the course gathered together a selection of potted plants from around the house. There were around ten plants in total and we had to choose one and communicate with it, listen to what it was saying or how it was feeling. To do this we were encouraged to enter a particular brainwave frequency (we had been shown how to do this). I was astounded when I heard the plant I'd chosen speak to me. I could hear a tiny and scared voice and it told me that some of the time it was fine but it would like more love, and some of the time it was freezing cold. When it came to having to report back to the group on our experiences I worried about being way off the mark. What on earth did it mean that the plant was saying it was freezing cold some of the time, yet not all the time? I worried I was hearing nonsense. Still, I went with what I got and my teachers glanced at each other and smiled and told me this plant was probably in need of more love as it didn't get as much attention as some of the other plants, and at the moment it was positioned right inside the doorway in the porch so that when someone pulled open the front door a cold blast of wind whipped inside, hitting this poor plant directly. So the plant had spoken to me very precisely by telling me that it wasn't cold *all the time*. I was amazed and excited. I never viewed plants in the same way again.

Twenty-Four

Around this time I recall going to the premiere of the film that Charlie had starred in. It had been made years ago in Wales but now the director had finally found a budget to edit it and commit it to celluloid. It wasn't on general release and he was looking for a distributor, but a few select screenings around London had been arranged. The April sky was beginning to darken following a dramatic sunset and the city lights began to blink and twinkle as we arrived at the Everyman cinema in Hampstead. Annie and I entered the building and made straight for the toilets but even as I pushed open the door I knew a vision I'd just had on the street was about to manifest. There was Danielle, towering above me in very high heels, wearing an air of thunder in her aura. At least we managed to say hello, but she left a decidedly icy vapour trail as she swung past me. Annie and I raised our eyebrows at each other and entered adjacent cubicles. Yes, I was used to it by now and I was determined that I wasn't going to allow her attitude to spoil the night. I also recognised that I was partly responsible for the iciness, if not the thunder too. Perhaps I needed to be friendlier. Perhaps she thought I was a stuck-up little madam? Either way, I didn't want to be at war with her, with him, with anyone. I wanted peace, even if I still wanted Charlie. Loving him shouldn't cause anyone any pain – and it didn't; pure love doesn't cause any pain, but learning to love unconditionally was still something I needed to work on.

Still, my next encounter with Danielle made extending a hand of friendship hard for me.

My Australian friend Ruth had joined us by now and we were queuing at the bar for drinks when Danielle spotted us and made straight for our end of the bar with one of her friends. I'm not quite sure how or why but she proceeded, gigglingly, to bash into both Annie and Ruth accidently-on-purpose. Luckily they were both mature enough to let it go. Still, the atmosphere was edgy, as was usually the case when Charlie, Danielle and I were under the same roof, and much as I tried not to let it bother me, my feathers were ruffled.

Yet, no matter what was going on, I was always delighted to see Charlie perform and I settled down happily in my seat as the house lights went down. I didn't know much about the film other than that Charlie was playing the role of an actor and it was set in the 70s with lots of drugs on the menu. The first scene of the film was an empty stage in what looked like an old Victorian music hall. A lone figure walked onto the stage. I knew his silhouette immediately and instinctively. There he stood, leaning sexily on a microphone stand, exuding his usual magnetism, looking ready to unleash something immensely powerful, something of his own, something that sank into people's souls and touched them. I was struck by his ability to emit so much emotion without saying anything. This was something Charlie often did in real life and it was quite strange to see him doing it right there on the screen. Charlie looked right into the camera and then the screen cut to a square of blackness, reopening in a few seconds on a street outside the music hall where another character stood pulling on a cigarette, turning up his collar to shield himself from the cold wind blowing in from quite likely the river Thames. I loved the film and thought Charlie's performance was inspired. For a few hours I lost myself in the film, being bathed by his beautiful voice, caressed by this special energy, happy just to see him even if it was on the screen rather than in the flesh, though I knew he was likely somewhere in the cinema, watching the film and himself.

After the screening there were after-show drinks happening in a nearby club, which Annie, Ruth and I went along to with most of the rest of the invited audience. It wasn't long before I noticed Charlie working his way over to the corner where we were chatting. He didn't come too close – just close enough to see properly and for me to see him. I felt he wanted me to approach him or at least wave or do *something* – but I purposefully didn't. As he hadn't answered my last call and had been growing increasingly distant I felt it was time to pull back. It wasn't something that came naturally to me where Charlie was concerned because I felt almost compelled to reach out to him. But I decided that if he wanted to speak with me he could easily find a way – so I just kept right on chatting to Annie and Ruth. He retreated briefly, but the next thing he did was sneak up somewhere behind us again and begin a conversation with some people who were positioned to our rear. I only know this because Annie told me afterwards. Quite probably he thought I would turn around and start chatting to him, as the Eileen of old would definitely have done, but that night I just kept my distance. Charlie finished the conversation with the people behind us and went away looking glum, and half an hour or so afterwards we left too.

I can't say I felt good about virtually ignoring Charlie offstage, but I was trying to break out of an old pattern. Perhaps I was wrong and he hadn't actually wanted interaction, yet I strongly sensed he wanted to connect – even if it was just a moment, a smile, an acknowledgement that I still loved him. I wanted the same thing, and part of me was kicking myself for holding back like I just had. There was another screening coming up in a few days with a question-and-answer session with Charlie and the director at Hudson's Cave, but I wasn't going to be there as Annie and I were heading off to Paris that weekend. I knew Charlie would expect me to be there as I rarely missed an event involving his work, especially at our familiar stomping ground. Perhaps he thought he'd speak to me then and everything would be OK. He had seemed sad and weary as he hung around at the after-show, and I did worry about him. Excited as I was about going to Paris I have to admit a part of me also wished I could catch the screening at the Cave as I wanted him to know I *did* still care. I wasn't any good at pretending I didn't care. I wasn't any good at pretending full stop, and pretending is never the answer. Still, there must be a better way of handling things than I had that night.

When I got to the most romantic city in the world a couple of days later, I did manage to put Charlie to one side. Not out of my head completely (is that possible?), but with new sights, sounds and smells to tickle my senses it was easier to divert my attention elsewhere. Being in Balham and its environs never helped with shifting my focus as there was always something there to remind me – every corner, every cafe, every bar, every paving stone, even the cherry blossom blowing in the wind seemed to carry a trace of his essence – but here in Paris I could temporarily, at least, enjoy other beautiful things… and Paris in the springtime is an incredibly beautiful place to be.

Something odd happened on the Sunday morning. I woke up with a violent sore throat. It literally came out of nowhere and was excruciatingly painful. I felt cranky and out of sorts, pissed off because this was our last day and I wanted to make the most of it. I sat in bed, whinging to Annie, drinking coffee and watching the news in French on the TV as I tried to work out how my throat could feel so bad out of the blue. Strangely enough, within hours when we were out and about in Montmartre my sore throat disappeared as swiftly as it had arrived. Although I was mystified, I wasn't complaining and was able to enjoy the remaining time in *La Ville Lumière*.

Back in London, a few days later, I bumped into Hudson buying an aubergine and some peppers at Hildreth Street Market. I was aware that the screening would have taken place on Saturday night and enquired how it had been.

"Oh, it was cancelled," Hudson told me, pocketing his change. "Charlie had a sore throat and lost his voice and the director guy buggered off somewhere else."

"Oh… right." I nodded, staring at the tower of

aubergines from which Hudson had made his selection. I told him I'd probably see him later in the bar and walked on, deep in thought. Was that sore throat significant or was I reading too much into things? Could Charlie's physical state affect mine? Could mine affect his? Did I temporarily pick up his sore throat through that unusual channel we shared? I'd never know for sure, of course.

Twenty-Five

I knew he somehow wasn't quite himself. He sat drinking a can of beer and I could sense an invisible wall around him. Straight away I knew I wasn't going to break through it and I didn't want to try because I guessed he was walling me off for a reason, for his own protection. I was disappointed as I felt out of touch and wanted to touch base in a real and meaningful way. With some people, superficial conversation was all I expected but with Charlie, it seemed particularly wrong not to be straight with each other, not to tell it like it is, not to drop the masks we too often present to the world. I got on with the interview, keenly aware that things felt very different between us.

We'd finally arranged to meet for a chat as the Last Exit Players had finally officially called it a day and were splintering off in different directions. At this point, they still had the rehearsal room near Balham Tube station but they'd soon be moving out of that space which they'd shared for so long. Charlie had asked me to the studio that evening, rather than meeting in a bar or one of our flats as we'd always done before. I immediately got the feeling this rendezvous was secret.

When I entered the studio I almost wondered if he had been sleeping there on and off – everything looked vaguely crumpled and strange and I had a sense that something was being concealed, but I felt disinclined to pry or prod. I knew something was wrong in some capacity but its nature was unclear and Charlie wasn't giving anything away, and somehow I knew that all the questioning in the world wasn't going to provide the answers – or not answers that made sense.

We hadn't seen each other for perhaps a month and I didn't feel he was especially bothered about that – that he'd had other priorities – whereas I'd been aching to see him. The usual affection that flowed between us, though not entirely absent, was muted. He answered my questions in a matter-of-fact, unemotional way that again, wasn't the style of the man I knew. I started to get the feeling he might even be *attempting* to drive me away, to get rid of me, that he was deliberately not engaging with me the way he normally did – not because he didn't care but because he couldn't handle it and had decided it was easier to just pull back than face this nameless, beautiful, bewildering energy; this relationship that currently was neither blossoming nor withering. No, it lay almost dormant, like a quivering rose under a blanket of frost, knowing it couldn't die but also that it couldn't burst out into the sunshine – at least not yet. It had to follow the route that the Universe demanded. It – or perhaps what I mean is Charlie and myself – we both had to transform from chrysalis to butterfly. We had individual journeys to make before being together was even a possibility, and maybe I was starting to really understand that now.

I was sad that things felt so flat between us but I tried to keep my feelings in check. We'd talked for about forty minutes and though I wasn't thrilled with the interview I had something useable, something worthy of putting in the magazine.

Charlie's phone rang. I could see Danielle's picture on the screen of his iPhone, so I knew it was her, but somehow I'd known that anyway. I guessed he hadn't told her where he was. I sank back into the leather chair I'd been sitting on, trying to allow him space to answer – if that was what he wanted or needed to do. He let it ring a few times, then pressed a button that stopped the ringing and his mental stress was palpable to me. He may have silenced the phone, but the ringing clearly didn't stop in either of our heads because we both made moves to wrap things up. I sensed he was going to be in trouble. I didn't want that for him but I refused to feel guilty about it because what were we doing that was wrong? Discussing his projects and plans for a magazine article was hardly a sin. That was why I was there and why he was there, and that was a real reason even if the air was thick with layer upon layer of unspoken and semi-spoken hints, hurts and hopes, love and desire, and countless other nuances of emotion lurking in the shadows of the studio. It wasn't as though we were about to engage in some illicit sexual tryst. If we were going to do that it would have happened years ago. Although I can't speak for Charlie, I know I felt there was nothing sordid about this love and I had no intention of sneaking around behind anyone else's back. I'm not saying there wasn't sexual tension between us at times because there was – but I think we both knew a sneaky affair was not part of our path. I was never going to be his bit on the side, his fallback girl, and he never even hinted he wanted me to be. We had too much respect for each other to take on those roles. This love was noble. It was honest, true and pure and unless we were both free and out in the open we weren't going down that road, no matter how much I loved him and no matter what he felt for me.

We got outside to see a pale and misty half-moon hanging over Balham. I waited while Charlie locked the door. As we turned from the studio he said, with a degree of urgency, "We'll have to meet up again soon."

"Yes, of course," I replied, surprised at this suggestion as I hadn't had the feeling he'd been comfortable about the whole meeting.

"Yeah, definitely," he said as we walked briskly towards the Tube station. Although we made some small talk there was still that distance between us. We parted company at the top of my road and I arrived home feeling quite down. Somehow, despite the noises he'd made about reconvening, I sensed it wasn't going to happen. I had a sensation that forces beyond my control were pulling us further and further apart.

The healing work I was doing was helping me but it didn't always feel that way, as delving into our wounds and facing the emotional sludge that's been deposited there can actually delude you into thinking you're getting worse, not better. That is, until you let that cloud clear and the sludge evaporate. I wasn't seeing much of Charlie and that still saddened me, though I was consciously trying to let it go. Sometimes I felt I was making progress and I could keep my interests and energy elsewhere but on other days I seemed to be fighting a losing battle. I still kept blaming myself for being weak and wondered if it would ever end. The trouble was that deep, deep down, no matter how bleak it seemed to be, I still felt in my soul that there would be a happy ending. I don't quite know where that feeling came from. Was it just because I felt I'd invested so much energy in it that I couldn't think otherwise? Was it because Zharha had always told me to have faith? Was it the continuous parade of signs and synchronicities that still to that day littered my path? Or was it just that I had always been the kind of person who keeps hope alive? It was impossible to say, but at this point the truth was that inner hope nudged me along despite the external reality not quite matching it. Yet, one of the lessons I was learning was that external realities are not always what they seem...

One such spine-shivering sign happened one day when I was feeling particularly confused and upset about the apparent lack of progress in my situation. In exasperation, I talked to the powers that be, the angels, the Universe, God? I sent my message up in a desperate plea for peace, for an end to the questions I tormented myself with – though really only I could stop that torment. I just couldn't recognise that yet. *If Charlie is the one for me, give me a clear sign*, I pleaded. I wanted this man so much. I was sure it was meant to be, yet here we were, so many years down the line, barely speaking. I asked for a sign to show me if it was indeed Charlie – or if it *wasn't* him and I was wrong about just about everything, that I could meet the man who was the right one and be set free from this torture. I visualised the 'right' man coming to me. I visualised a man coming from behind and placing a hand on my shoulder, a very loving and gentle touch. I deliberately didn't ask to see his face because I knew if I did it would morph into Charlie's and I wanted to be open to the possibility that it *could* be someone else. I felt that touch on my shoulder as though it was real and trusted that my plea had been heard by whoever had the power to send me that sign. Then I went about my business as normal, feeling a bit lighter and accepting that what was meant to be would be.

The next evening, Annie, Ruth and I met for drinks at a new bar doubling as an art gallery that had opened up near London Bridge. It was a quirky venue, and strangely a bit like the old music hall that featured in Charlie's recent film. There was a slightly rickety balcony on one side with space for around twenty people to be seated up there. I was immediately drawn to go up on the balcony, not because it gave me a bird's eye view of the gallery especially, just a sudden impulse. We climbed the creaky stairs and sat chatting with our drinks, watching the people below and admiring the artwork scattered around the different wall spaces.

My heart leapt when I suddenly saw Charlie standing with Danielle down below us.

"It's Charlie and Danielle," I whispered to Annie, who'd just observed them also. Annie, Ruth and I could barely contain our giggles when he appeared to point up to the balcony where we were sitting as though to suggest going up there, then clock us and pause with his finger in mid-air, then carry on talking, trying too hard to be normal. My hunch was that the mysterious force that often drew us together had caused him to gravitate towards the balcony, and then when he realised we were there, he was kind of happily shocked. Next thing I knew, to my amazement he and Danielle headed for the balcony stairs and came up also, sitting at the far end, as far away from us as was possible. It was a bit of a strange thing to do as I assumed Danielle wouldn't want to be anywhere near me or allow him to be, but perhaps she hadn't realised we were there.

The only reason I'm describing this odd scene is because of what happened five minutes later when Charlie and Danielle descended the stairs again. I hadn't even realised they were going back down until I suddenly felt a hand on my shoulder. It was a loving hand, a gentle hand, a reassuring hand. I turned and saw Charlie smile and give me a thumbs-up sign as he climbed down the stairs which ran directly behind me.

"I don't believe it," I muttered to Annie. I could still feel the warmth on my shoulder. I instantly remembered my request from the day before and I understood the sign I had been given. It had that swirling cosmic energy, that knowingness, that sense of mysterious but powerful forces being at work. Ultimately, it was a clear demonstration that this was beyond my control and was bigger than me; than him – that it *was* supposed to be him I was meant to be with. I wasn't off track. This was real. This experience did renew my hope, but at the same time I didn't know if it seemed right to just wait for things to resolve. He was worth waiting for, but how long can you wait for someone? Should you *ever* wait for someone? My instinct was no, yet this is what I kept finding myself doing, and then I kept trying to tear my focus away from him. It was a daily challenge and I just couldn't see how to break the habit. Though I wasn't completely drowning in quicksand, I was still generally stuck.

There was something else I noticed was starting to happen with Charlie. I was occasionally finding myself getting angry with him, which had never really been the case before. In the past if there was even a minor issue between us we had both had tended to go out of our way to resolve it, but now I felt I was starting to show my disapproval more if he gave me cause to disapprove, and unfortunately he did on a few occasions around this time. A situation arose where I spoke my mind with him in a way I'd never been pushed to before. Perhaps I just had to attempt to break the endlessly repeating cycle. We'd been in a loop for a long time. It may have been a loop that held a whole lot of love, but it was taking its toll on me, whether I wanted to fully admit that or not.

The reason my anger was sparked was a broken agreement. He'd agreed to come round for an interview at my place one Saturday morning. He never showed up and sent no message of excuse or apology. Somehow it was what I was expecting deep down because he'd been slowly retreating for months. I realised I was allowing him to treat me in this seemingly indifferent way and that wasn't OK. If I'd sat with it for a few days I probably would have just let it go, shrugged and let it be, thinking there'd be a good reason, but my spirit was fired up and even though I didn't want to hurt him, I didn't want him to hurt me either. When he didn't show up and an hour had gone by I decided I was going to let him know this wasn't any way to treat a friend. As calmly as possible I dialled his number and spoke to his disembodied voicemail, telling him that I'd appreciate it if, in the event that he couldn't keep an arrangement, he'd let me know, and that I thought we should leave the interview until he was good and ready. When I hung up I was shocked at myself for speaking to him like that. It didn't feel good but I felt a little bit more empowered than if I had I just said nothing. Yet, I also felt I'd hurt him and I couldn't bear to hurt him.

Still, it had felt important to make my stand even though I was uncomfortable with it. I wasn't expecting to hear anything from him now. Maybe this was for the best and would help me put him aside once and for all and move on. *Move on!* Metaphorically I stripped my bed of its old, crinkled sheets and lay down a fresh, clean white one. I threw the bottom sheet up towards the ceiling in an attempt to align it neatly, to flood my world with new energy, smoothing it down to get rid of the weary creases caused by too much tossing and turning. This was my new headspace. How long could I keep it clear without Charlie wandering back in?

A strange inner metamorphosis seemed to be occurring. My brain was whirring; my heart was bewildered. I felt as though I'd been pushed into a cement mixer and was being rocked about for a while before I could be transmuted into a new mix, shape or form. I couldn't really decipher the root of this change but it seemed to be happening whether I liked it or not.

I wanted to put the Charlie situation behind me more than ever (unless he did something radical, which I wanted even more). For probably the first time ever I considered that maybe I needed to stop seeing him completely, even though I only saw him briefly these days.

I wanted to be with whoever it was I was meant to be with – and get rid of the ghost of Charlie if this was all he was ever going to be, for that's what it felt like he was becoming. There was a sense that I was coming close to some kind of conclusion or breakthrough but it was currently still obscured. A scramble of rearrangements felt as though they were taking place and I watched the landscape nervously to see if dawn was going to break, or if the darkness would hover for longer.

Luckily for me, I did have Zharha, who managed to understand this peculiar energetic pattern better than most.

"I don't think there is anything wrong with the way you are feeling because, at the end of the day (and I am OK with this for this reason), you want to let go and you want to hold on," she said sensibly when I went to see her in Chelsea again. "Unfortunately if I told you to stop feeling this way and just completely let go, it would really throw you off so we just have to find creative ways of chipping away at it until you are ready to let it go. There is that strong feeling that if you truly let go you are giving up. Don't be disappointed... it was bound to happen once or twice. Be gentle with yourself." She offered me some squares of home-made chocolate cake on a small silver tray, and I felt momentarily better.

Still, chocolate cake can only help for a short while. I decided I would make more effort to get past the all-consuming pull he seemed to exert on me. I still had trouble believing that I could potentially be as happy with another man, but I tried to convince myself it must be possible. Of *course* it must be possible. There are millions of people in the world and why should I be singled out for this one, and only this one, no matter how perfect he seemed in so many ways? If he was incapable or unwilling to step up or didn't want what I did, despite his non-verbal signals, then I'd been mistaken, hadn't I? No, this couldn't be the way it was for eternity. I refused to believe I was doomed.

I did join an online dating site for a short time, slowly dipping my toe in a world that simply felt alien to me. Though the very idea went against my instincts I thought I would have to at least give it a go if I wanted to be a normal person and have a normal relationship. I interacted with a few guys and even arranged to meet some but somehow nothing felt right. I knew this style of meeting people just wasn't for me.

There were a few men during the years since I'd met Charlie I felt an attraction to. It wasn't as though I didn't notice anyone else, but even when I felt an attraction and got to a position where I could imagine myself with them, something inevitably seemed to happen so that the relationship either stopped dead in its tracks or the person would strangely disappear, or something would be revealed that made them clearly not a viable option. In most cases, the man in question just seemed to disappear overnight, as though he'd been magically whisked away. This actually happened recently yet again.

I had been enjoying the attention of a particular bartender who had recently started working in Cafe Noir. I mentioned to Annie one evening that he was attractive, adding jokily that now that I'd articulated that he would disappear – as had already happened several times with several men before. I would find myself feeling mildly disappointed when this happened. I couldn't tell if this was something in me pushing them away or something from the Universe saying, *No, no, he's not the one – don't get bogged down in this. You know who the one for you is!* Annie and I were shocked when the bartender simply disappeared overnight, as though he'd vanished in a puff of smoke. How and why? I had no idea what to think.

Charlie never seemed to fade. The intensity did vary a little from time to time, and sometimes I'd go through a short time where he seemed to be keeping in the background energetically speaking, but there were other times where he seemed to be inside my head 24/7. I was fighting his omnipresence, which I think made it worse. What I probably needed to do, I know now, is just accept that we are connected and that he's never far away, but instead I just kept blaming myself for failing at letting him go.

It also seemed to happen strongly when I had made progress, when I had succeeded in focusing my energy elsewhere. Suddenly I'd be engulfed in a memory or a longing to see him that struck as hard as ever. I'd then feel I was regressing even though I was consciously fighting the pull. I'd berate myself for being weak and nostalgic and unable to consistently move forward.

'Regressing' may be too strong a word, but the almighty tug that made me think of him felt beyond my control. I wrote an email to Zharha:

Though I'm looking forwards, considering there are other options – there MUST be – I just keep feeling pulled back to

Charlie and this huge feeling of unfinished business. I thought I'd got past that feeling too, but it's there. I don't know if there's anything that can be done other than just trying to let it go... I don't want to beat myself up about it as that's pointless too, but why can't I move on properly? I feel something is wrong with me — even though I also know I HAVE made progress.

Twenty – Six

That summer, the good news was that several times, I glimpsed new possibilities – they may just have been glimpses, like a spotlight suddenly revealing a path that then rapidly disappeared, but I had a very real feeling of forward motion that I hadn't really had before. I also sensed, for maybe the first time since this crazy journey began, that I could truly stand on my own and see myself as separate from Charlie. Even though that notion scared me a little, it was actually a good and strengthening feeling. I still found that none of this really made sense but I was getting closer to realising that it didn't have to. It was what it was. It is what it is. I wanted to let my life lead me to wherever I was meant to be (although I also thought maybe I should stop using phrases like 'meant to be'…).

I was still working through stuff with Zharha and she pointed out that I had a lot of guilt attached to moving on from Charlie. She explained that it was most likely fired by past life residues as there seemed little in our current history to make me feel so incredibly guilty for trying to let him go and get on with my life. The past life baggage was huge and even though I had very little conscious memory of the lives I believed our souls had shared, that didn't negate their impact. The imprint of other times and places, deeds and deals, lessons that hadn't been completed, these karmic relics lie beneath the soil of our unconscious minds whether we dig and unearth them or not. They still influence us, or this was certainly my understanding. Zharha helped me to forgive myself for feeling this way. She gently encouraged me to find ways of energetically freeing myself. I still didn't truly want to separate from Charlie but I reasoned it was vital for allowing anything else to happen with anyone else. I wanted to be healthy and free.

In my mind, I had an odd image… a bit like he and I had been asleep in each other's arms for years and years, locked together in a sleeping embrace, but now I had risen and left him sleeping there. I even felt I could cover him up and tuck him in knowing he would be OK, but that I had to leave and get on with things. I didn't quite know where this feeling had come from but it was liberating. I was slowly shedding the guilt attached to leaving/separating since I knew he was safe and he could choose to rise too if he wanted.

I'd said happily to Zharha the last time we spoke on the phone that seeing him didn't seem to be throwing me like it used to. This was only a few days before an encounter one evening in Cafe Noir that stung me badly. I suspect it stung him too, which only added to our joint pain pool. My mother was visiting from Manchester and Annie and I had taken her out for dinner. The wine was chilled, the ambience was warm and mellow and our food was mouth-wateringly good. We chatted happily and I felt at peace. Then a group of three entered the establishment. I lifted my head to see Charlie and Danielle and that friend of his, Keith. My previously intact poise started to dissolve on the spot, but I kept as calm and normal as possible on the outside. They seated themselves opposite us, ordered drinks and somehow seemed to create a lot of noise, collectively generating a type of energy that bounced boisterously off the walls, like somebody aimlessly kicking a football around.

Usually when Charlie showed up I was eager to say hello but this time, I felt I'd done so much hard work on releasing him that I really didn't want to get dragged back into the drama. So I hadn't waved or even acknowledged them especially, without being what I considered rude. I assumed he noticed, even if unconsciously, because within a short time he came over to our table.

Before I had a chance to speak or introduce my mum he said, "Hello, Eileen, my love. How's it going?" I was shocked to hear him use the words 'my love', yet at the same time, despite appearances, I knew I *was* his love. I got the impression he was either a little drunk or a little drugged, though not seriously so – just mildly tipsy. For some reason I couldn't react. I know I responded in some way but it was short and by no means my usual affectionate type of greeting.

When he didn't get a gushing response he tried to get Annie's attention by poking her playfully in the arm. When she didn't really give him much response either, knowing the full story, he seemed to begin to panic. Even though I'd been polite, he had clearly picked up a change. He looked me in the eye and it was as though his thoughts had jumped out of his head, and though he wasn't speaking verbally I could hear him speak and the words were, *You don't love me any more?!* phrased half as a question and

171

half as a shocked statement. It was as though I'd physically slapped him. I felt him wobbling briefly as he stood before us, as though in danger of falling down, followed by walking with a heavy heart back to Danielle and Keith. I felt furious with him for playing games, as that's what it felt like he was doing since he'd walked in the door. I was dimly aware that Danielle seemed furious too when he returned to their table but my main focus was on trying to appear outwardly normal as I didn't want to have to explain any of this to my mum. I didn't want her to know what I'd been going through and even if I did attempt to tell her it wouldn't make any sense, so we carried on our meal and I tried to brush what had happened under the red paper table cloth, but it was near impossible as I could hear his unspoken words echoing all around Cafe Noir. *You don't love me any more?!*

The thing is, I did love him, and do love him, but I was learning I could love him without loving aspects of his behaviour. This was a big step for me.

Somehow I got through the rest of the meal and kept it together but I wished it hadn't happened. I was doing so well. Yet, I also knew I was OK and though I was ruffled I hadn't allowed myself to be hooked back in. Still, I lay in bed that night in torment. I'm not sure how much of it was my torment and how much of it was his. I was determined though that I wouldn't just cave in and slide back into the trapped space I'd occupied for so long... being there for him ceaselessly, loving him ceaselessly, waiting for him ceaselessly. I did feel guilty though. I felt cruel even though logically I knew there was nothing cruel about my behaviour. It wasn't as though I'd told him to go to hell. Yet, there was a sense of him being in hell. Perhaps he *was* in some kind of hell but if so, it wasn't my fault, was it?

Luckily, I still had Zharha to discuss things with and we talked for some time about what was going on. She explained to me how deep and old (as in centuries of past lives) our connection was, and that him talking to me on the astral plane was very real and how much it was bound to pull me if I didn't find a way of dealing with it. Although I still had some difficulty fully accepting how rampant our energetic exchanges at night were, I knew something major was happening. There was no other explanation for the hours I spent unable to sleep, literally feeling tugged back and forth. He didn't want me to let him go. I didn't *want* to let *him* go, but how could we go on like this? Why couldn't we just work it out or even talk about it in our daily lives? I was aware that to even attempt to would send him running for the hills, if he wasn't already *in* the hills. But even from those remote and misty hills he found ways of popping back and forth to check I was still there. I could understand his fear, his frustration and anguish on some level. I hoped he could understand mine. But what should be done? What could be done? Zharha felt we needed some kind of separation spiritually. Although we weren't seeing much of each other these days in the physical world, our interaction had never been confined to that, so that didn't really solve anything.

She told me she'd weave something she called a 'dream shield'. It should keep us less tangled up on the astral plane, keep a healthy distance so the pulling and tugging would be less intense. Part of me was sad to think we needed a wall of sorts between us, yet I acknowledged that this pulling was very real and made it difficult to get on with my life. I still didn't really want to let him go, but I was worried about how powerful this hold was. I knew it was a good idea to try to minimise the interference seeing as our relationship on the physical plane seemed to be at a standstill. The dream shield seemed to work, to some extent. He did break through occasionally – or else I broke through; hard to say – but that was fine. Although I still missed him, I wasn't constantly being pulled about like a buoy on a stormy sea for the first time in many years, after Zharha did whatever it was she did.

Twenty – Seven

Still, it wasn't plain sailing either, even with the dream shield. During the process of attempting to let go, yet again, for no apparent reason I found that I was suddenly drowning in a flood of memories of how I first met Charlie and how destined it felt. I spilled this out to Zharha in another email, trying to make sense of the torrent of emotion that washed over me afresh, just when I thought I'd managed to find a delicate balance.

I always knew when I made that choice to go to London that I was also going (or really going) to meet the love of my life there – that I was called. I have never really told anyone other than Annie that, as clear as it was to me, because I didn't think anyone would have believed me. But within days of moving to London – BAM! He manifested right before my eyes and I was shocked. London isn't a small place either – it's a big city and we could have both lived here for 20 years and never encountered each other.

So within days I'd seen him and within weeks I knew that's why I was really sent here (or a BIG part of the reason why) and that I was being given the most amazing gift the Universe could give me, my dream man, just as I foresaw him and then it started to become more and more obvious that he was feeling it too (at least on some level) and it seemed so fated and beautiful. I think what I'm trying to say is it's hard to let go of that gift I felt I was presented with – even though things haven't gone the way I thought/felt they would/should because this kind of thing surely doesn't happen for no reason. And even now, when we rarely see each other and rarely speak, I still can feel this bond burn so brightly between us, like this unquenchable flame, and when I think of moving on, meeting someone new, it feels like I am being asked to quench that flame and some part of me feels it's not meant to be quenched.

Having said all that, and sorry for the essay, I know I can't stay in this state forever, with nothing happening despite the flame/the feelings etc., so I do have to find a way around it and I am willing and even wanting someone I can love and who loves me too – I just don't want to 'throw away' (if that is the right term) what I have been given, even if you could argue that I haven't really been given it because we're not together. I hope this makes sense and I hope we can find a way for me to move past this. I do think I AM moving past it but an inch at a time, which seems to be all I can manage.

I was sitting sorrowfully by the computer after writing this epistle, lamenting and celebrating the enormity of it all, when my phone buzzed with a text. It was Zharha: *Lunch, tomorrow? Taz? Bloomsbury?* Taz was a wonderful Turkish restaurant I'd visited once before with Zharha. How could I refuse?

"Eileen, do you have any idea how frustrating it is for me (can't speak for anyone else) to *see* what should happen, to see the dynamics unfolding and then watch as they disintegrate (with his own disintegration), to watch other people who *know* they are supposed to be out of the lives of the people that they are making miserable, to watch people run from the very thing they want to run towards? Believe me, I get your frustration totally," Zharha told me, tossing open her serviette and eyeing a beautiful pomegranate salad dish that was being carried by. "That looks very, very good!"

I agreed about the dish and about the frustration.

"Wine?" Zharha grinned at me.

"Er, yeah, why not?" I grinned back. We both consulted our menus in silence for a moment before a waiter arrived to take our order.

"The fact that I can't do anything about it drives me crazy," Zharha went on when we'd placed our order, "and what's worse, I do admit that I was unequivocally wrong (something I do with difficulty much of the time), but I have learned over the last year or so that we psychics and healers are not God and we see paths but are not necessarily able to say without a shadow of a doubt that someone will take that path, even if it is the best path for them. I agree with you totally about frustration. I have thought about this so much. I can't even make excuses because I don't know *why* this got so difficult, except to say that there was much that probably needed to come out to be healed and he may need to learn some tough lessons that he couldn't have learned any other way."

I opened my mouth to speak, wanting so much to tell her I didn't blame her in the slightest for being wrong, but the waiter returned with a basket of fresh bread.

"Eileen, I must urge you strongly not to live in the past because it won't help, and his choices didn't just affect you two being together, rather, his whole life, and there may very well be a reason all this is happening that even I can't see. You're clearing a lot out, not just from Charlie, but from life as a whole. It could be helping you grow in ways you needed to grow as well. You're in a much different place now. At the end of the day, what isn't arguable is there *is* love here, on both parts, but he has totally screwed up his own life and that has to be unscrewed at this point before he can ever let anyone in. I am deeply sorry for being so totally wrong about him coming towards you (though you must admit there have been times you have been teetering on the brink... *many* more times that I care to count), and I can't even tell you why because, to be honest, he *knows* what would be better for him. He knows *who* would be better for him. What he's doing now is such a mystery to me as to why people, not just him, have to drag themselves down, and for what reason?"

It was an epic speech and good for me to hear, and not for a moment did I blame Zharha for being 'wrong', as she put it.

"I do know it is frustrating for you," I said with a sigh, "and honestly I really don't blame you for being 'wrong' because I entirely agree that it was on the brink of 'happening'. It felt like it couldn't really go any other way. I see it myself, or I saw it myself, and I can't explain it either so I don't expect you to. The thing is I now have the urge to face it – to face that it hasn't gone the way we both thought it would, and hopefully by facing it I can let it go and leave it all behind. I know he knows it too. That's another aspect of it that's so frustrating." I reached for some bread at the same time as Zharha, and we laughed.

"He does know it," she said, "but knowing it is one

thing. Doing something about it…" She shrugged. "Only he can decide that."

"But there is a way out of this." I buttered my bread with quiet determination. "I'm convinced of that. Even if it takes a bit longer. I'm determined to be happy with or without him. Thanks for understanding, and please know this wasn't me pointing the finger at anyone. You've helped me more than maybe you'll ever know and I thank God for you being there for me throughout all this."

My eyes were tearing up and the restaurant became a blur, but it needed to be said. This woman meant so much to me and I was so grateful to have her, as well as Annie, to speak with about all this crazy stuff. "I think part of the problem for me is I do still see Charlie finally doing what I thought he'd do long ago, and I have weird waking (and sleeping) visions of him knocking on the door and standing there smiling, not speaking but not needing to. This could be wishful thinking or there could be some part of me that knows I may get my heart's desire after all. But I know, oh yes, I completely know I have to live my life and I can't wait for that. This is what I'm really trying to do, and all this stuff that's coming up I'm sure is because I really, seriously am trying to move beyond this. And like you said, there could be (must be) a reason this has all gone the way it has. I do know that – I have learned a lot."

Zharha digested what I'd said along with the gorgeous, freshly baked bread, then spoke with so much love in her voice I wanted to cry again.

"This stuff is *really* tough to deal with," she said. "I expected what you are going through, and couldn't do

anything really to stop it because it was you fighting...
that's why I said, it's OK that it is step by step because you
just can't try to let go cold turkey. Now, onto what I really
want to say. Don't ever worry about writing me essays
and I understand *totally* what you mean by not wanting
to let go of the gift you indeed *were* given... and nobody,
not even me, is telling you not to be grateful and I would
not say you really haven't been given the gift just because
you aren't with him. In fact, I told you the other day that
bond may never be broken. The thing I am wanting to do
is make it so that connection doesn't interfere with you
living your life to the fullest, even if, based on his decisions
and lack of movement, that means with someone else.
Right now, even with all the work we've done, your core
level doesn't *want* to let go – not that it can't, it can, but it
simply doesn't want it.

"I know all about what you speak. I believe you
thoroughly... I know how hard it is after you have *seen*
manifestation at its best to let go because you think it is
like slapping the Universe in the face for the gift you've
been given. The thing is, we have to figure a way for it to
be manageable because it is interfering with you living a
happy life: you are happy, but not as happy as you want
to be. It *is* a gift and it *is* a connection – it's very real –
but it is also up to him to take the steps towards you, and
Eileen, unless he straightens out his own life, that can't
happen. You being able to talk about this experience is
very touching to me and I am honoured that you shared
it, and second, it's crucial to being able to manage it, so it
isn't keeping you from living life to the fullest."

We had a long talk, some smooth, plummy wine, some

truly nourishing food and a big hug when we rose from the table. By the time we left the restaurant and I rejoined the swarms of people moving up and down Oxford Street I was in a better place. I was so lucky. I was lucky not just to have met Charlie, but to have met Zharha, to have met Annie, my family and just about everyone in my life – no, *everyone* in my life. There's always a purpose. It may not be obvious. Everything happens for a reason and sometimes the reason is not revealed until you are ready to appreciate it – or even see it, and that can take a long time sometimes.

Twenty-Eight

It was around this time that the Universe created another unusual convergence of time and place and people. Annie and I had planned to take a week to go to the Edinburgh Festival that year. Neither of us had ever been before and it was something we'd both always wanted to do. Excitedly we'd booked our hotel and train a couple of months before. We'd reached the point where this upcoming break now gleamed welcomingly on the horizon. It felt like just what I needed. Shortly after that last difficult encounter with Charlie in Cafe Noir, I found myself looking at the Edinburgh Festival website to consider what we might need to buy tickets for in advance. I was astounded to see Charlie Gitane's name on the listings. The letters of his name jumped out at me like a fire alarm in my soul and I had to double-check to make sure I wasn't hallucinating. He was appearing in a one-off production in Edinburgh on the Saturday we were due to arrive to start our holiday. This perhaps wouldn't have been so strange if the Last Exit Players were still together and touring regularly. But no, Charlie had been involved in only two or three shows in the past year and all of those had been very low-key and on home ground. What were the chances of him doing a one-off gig in Edinburgh on the exact date Annie and I were scheduled to go?

"What?! Are you serious?" gasped Annie when I told her. "Now that *is* weird!" Even with weird being a decidedly relative quality these days, this arrangement seemed strangely fated. Deep inside, I knew whatever happened there would be significant, and I wasn't wrong.

I've always been prone to headaches – even as a child they were common enough. Sometimes they explode into full-blown migraines, sometimes horrid cluster headaches that keep marching angrily from one room in my skull to another, banging the door of each room loudly as they exit and enter another. Sometimes, fortunately, they are just mild fuzziness that dissipates quickly. In the last few years, I'd noticed that my headaches seemed to have become slightly more frequent, often following emotional upsets. Sometimes a glass of wine was enough to trigger one, where previously I could drink without any problems. Likewise, a hormonal trigger at a particular time of the month was becoming more common. Once in a while, like the one that came at *this* time, they had no obvious cause – or not one I was aware of at the time. With hindsight though, I feel sure I know what triggered the beast of a headache that got hold of me that summer. This one worried me because it was so severe and so prolonged and so unexplainable by any of the usual cues.

It went on for days. I wanted to throw up much of the time, yet I couldn't. I wondered if I had a virus but at the end of day, it didn't feel like a virus. It just felt like my body was rebelling against something, straining horribly. It got so bad that for some of the time I could barely lift my head from the pillow or cushion or wherever I achingly laid it. I considered going to the doctor but somehow didn't think

183

it would solve matters. They'd tell me to swallow a few painkillers and lie in a darkened room. In desperation I contacted Zharha, who I knew would do anything and everything she could. She was concerned and perplexed by it too, but she worked on my poor aching head and after another twenty-four hours or so it finally relented and I gratefully felt normality seeping back in. I thanked the mighty Zharha for all her help and with relief, went about my normal business.

I was due to conduct an interview with a local songstress named Wendy May one summer evening just before my birthday. I'd known Wendy for a while and we had a good, giggly bond so I was looking forward to seeing her as I strolled along Balham High Road for our scheduled rendezvous in Hudson's Cave. I hadn't been in the Cave for months. My life seemed to be veering away from many of the people I'd known in that circle as I searched for ways to find my balance. It was also part of my attempt to let Charlie go, because even though he didn't drop into the bar as much as he used to, we had so much history there it was impossible not to get at least a whiff of the memories. They were scrawled in the old posters that lined the walls, huddled invisibly in the empty seats and sofas we'd shared on so many occasions, and of course Hudson himself was always talking about Charlie – or he was whenever he saw me.

As I neared the traffic lights that preceded the turning onto the road where Hudson's Cave was snuggled near the railway bridge, I had a strange experience. I can remember precisely where my feet were on the street and precisely the view across the road to a block of flats.

It was against this mundane backdrop that I received a very clear and factual message. It said, *Hudson is going to tell you that Charlie is getting married*. It wasn't one specific voice; there was no clap of thunder or anything out of the ordinary in the air at all. But it was as distinctive as if someone had just walked up to me in the street and delivered this information. I heard it and it seemed to come from somewhere way, way up in the sky, higher than the aeroplanes, higher than the clouds My response was a kind of blank wonder followed by a desire to try and cancel out such a thought. Surely not. Why now? But somehow I knew I couldn't dismiss it. Turning down the road that led to the Cave, I put it aside in some back room of my mind and pushed in through the old, familiar door.

Hudson was alone behind the bar and the Cave was practically empty. Wendy hadn't arrived yet. Within a minute or so of me being in the building Hudson spoke a short sentence that sent me inwardly reeling, though somehow I remained standing.

"Charlie's got engaged!" he said in a bouncy, excited way. Having never known for sure how much Hudson knew about Charlie and myself and our unusual bond, I couldn't tell if he was genuinely excited by the news or just getting some slightly sick kick by breaking it to me.

I suspected the latter, and did everything in my power to remain as normal as possible. I probably said something like, "Oh, really?" which I suppose isn't normal at all. I sure as hell wasn't going to let Hudson know this had immediately pierced me. I was thankful for the warning I'd received on the street even though I was nearly as shocked by its accuracy as by the news itself...

even though on a very, very deep, almost imperceptible level I wasn't surprised at all.

Wendy turned up and for the next couple of hours I used every muscle of my power to pretend everything was OK. She performed a few songs and I sat watching, inwardly flinching with pain, hoping that the avalanche of tears could be kept at bay for a little longer and that nothing was spilling out of the corners of my eyes. Hudson had wittered on about an engagement party or gathering but I hadn't taken in the details. Somehow I attempted to bury the news for later, for when I was alone or at least with somebody who'd understand, like Annie. Even though it felt unreal, I knew it *was* real and this wasn't some cruel joke. *How could he? How could he?* was all my heart could mutter, and I shuddered while trying to focus on Wendy's conversation. I left about two hours later, feeling I just couldn't hide the enormous wave of hurt that was welling up inside me. Feeling guilty about not being very present for Wendy I said goodbye, telling myself I would explain and apologise when I'd had time to digest this bombshell. I think it was raining as I walked myself home. In fact, it was pouring.

Now I was home. Annie was getting ready for bed. I told her the news, crumpling up in pain, starting to lash out in anger at Charlie by now. I felt betrayed in a way I never had before, as though a sacred agreement had been torn asunder. As the loud rain pelted down out on the shiny, dark street below the window, I had a sense the heavens were sharing my anguished anger. I remember telling Annie I needed a drink and we opened a bottle of wine that had been lurking apologetically in the kitchen as though it knew it might be needed – but not for my birthday celebrations the next day, rather for commiserations. I wasn't normally one to seek comfort in alcohol. I tend to drink to celebrate, to toast or just in a social bonding type of manner. But there was no denying that this time I reached for a glass to blur the sharpness of the knife twisting its way through my heart. I had to numb it, or attempt to.

Annie was as shocked as I was. She kindly sat with me in my bedroom on a clean white duvet-covered bed and had a drink with me. I decided I didn't want to go any further into that bottle of red, though it would have been easy. I told Annie to go to bed and that I would too and I'd be fine. The rest of the night no longer registers in my memory other than lying down with that choking pain and the sense that nature had somehow gone off course. This wasn't supposed to happen. It had happened, though, and in the morning I'd figure out what to do. *There must be something I can do. There must be something I can say. There must be... a reason.*

Twenty - Nine

My birthday had arrived. The sun had risen, though it was hidden behind a solid wall of darkening clouds. There I lay under my snow-white duvet. There on the floor also lay a sad, empty glass with a film of deep red wine hugging its lower walls. That vision of the glass confirmed last night hadn't been a dream, but the sickening feeling in my stomach knew that anyway. I was glad I hadn't made any birthday plans this year, hadn't invited anyone round or arranged drinks or even a small party, almost like part of me had known this sudden and strange artillery shell was going to crash-land on my birthday lawn. I had booked the day off work though, and that was a blessing. I didn't have to face anyone other than dear Annie. The noisy rain returned outside as though the soundtrack of yesterday had been placed back on the stereo. Were the heavens still angry? It wasn't supposed to rain this much in summer. It wasn't supposed to still hurt this much, was it? Hadn't I been in the midst of letting Charlie go anyway? That had been my aim for the past few months so shouldn't this news almost help me along that path?

That was a yes and a no. This news certainly did make me want to cease contact with him. It changed everything. He'd done the unthinkable, even though some would say what difference did it make when he was with Danielle anyway? Why did marrying her make it so much worse?

I think it was partly because I felt this wasn't what he really wanted to do. I'd never believed Charlie was in love with Danielle or even wanted a long-term relationship, let alone to be her husband. It just felt like a huge mistake, regardless of my place in the situation. So why would he do it? Too gutless to say no? Or could I be so wrong, so blind that I failed to see that he did love her? *Could* he want this? Though my gut gave a resounding 'no' to that question, it really wasn't for me to answer and that's one of the things I had to (painfully) learn here. Though I'd never believed that marrying someone proved anything about depth of feeling, it was a commitment that sent a message to the world that 'this is the one I love'. He was making his choice and I had to respect that.

My choice on that day was to move on. I still didn't quite know how but I was determined. This was the end. I went backwards and forwards from sad to angry but didn't waver from the sudden feeling of finality, the feeling that had eluded me for so long. It was hard to believe at this moment that I genuinely felt I never wanted to see him again, never wanted to see that longing look on his face or in his eyes. At least, if there was a positive, it was that. His choice, daft as it seemed to me, had provided me with the fuel to never look back.

Annie and I were sitting in a cafe bar in Waterloo, having had a stroll along the South Bank. I loved walking by the Thames. It felt ancient and awesome and somehow soothing, even on a day like this. The rain chased us along and as it was getting progressively heavier we took shelter.

I didn't need it to be my birthday to order chocolate fudge cake with lashings of cream, but seeing as it *was* my birthday it felt pretty essential. I stared into the swirling pool of gooey chocolate as it mingled with the pure white cream. These stark contrasts of purity and murkiness had become more pronounced lately, like the red wine kissing the bottom of that glass against the backdrop of my white duvet cover the night before. The intensity of colour and definition in everything I saw had magnified for some reason. Perhaps it was just symbolic of my feeling that something so vibrant, so clean and bright as the love I felt for Charlie had been somehow sullied by his recent decision. The rain kept falling as Annie I talked about this and that, about Charlie and the absurdity of the news as we saw it, about a friend of Annie's who was causing her some upset, about trivia and chocolate cake and the unseasonal June weather. As I looked at other people in the cafe all going about their business, caught up in the lunchtime London bustle, it seemed my own life had become a shade more surreal. I knew I'd remember this South Bank scene even as it was happening, and I do, even though a lot of rainy water has washed under Charing Cross Bridge since that day.

I knew what had happened was going to take me a while to get my head around, and I wasn't sure how long that would be. It would surely happen; my head could do a lot of things if I worked on it. My soul was another matter though, and I had a feeling it had gone into shock and was not quite present right now, as though it had somehow been dislodged. Perhaps it was out there, walking by the banks of the Thames in the rain, staring forlornly at the never-ending raindrops smacking into the great, grey river. Some inner part of me had just wandered off, unable to process this new pivotal moment – this parting of ways, this wrench, this knife, this jolt I just hadn't seen coming. Still, my soul could only wander off and avert its gaze for so long. After all, I've always been the type to face facts. Part of the problem was I felt the facts were unclear. The truth was murky. The engagement had happened, I was sure about that, but I kept sensing Charlie's involvement was marginal, like he'd just nodded his head vaguely and was drifting into the arrangement in a half-arsed, half-baked, shrugging manner. I was basing this on a feeling, not on anything I'd seen, but a few days later I saw something that seemed to back it up, at least to some degree. I'd also learned quite a bit about trusting my instincts.

Thirty

A couple of days later, Annie and I were heading for Cafe Noir, which was our usual drinking den at that particular time. Still semi-zombified due to the recent news, I wasn't happy but I was coping, still intending to let him go and break any contact, to move on. How I hated that term. It never felt right in this particular situation and seemed to imply I'd been hanging around stupidly when I knew that wasn't true, no matter how it might appear to the average onlooker. I knew I'd met the love of my life – someone I always knew I'd meet – which is why I was having such a hard time taking in the fact that he appeared not to see it the same way.

When we were still a good distance from the bar I mentioned to Annie that I felt he was around. This was by no means an uncommon thing for me to sense as I often picked him up in the ether long before a physical manifestation. I was hoping I was wrong this time as I was still adamant that I didn't want to see him. It would make it all too harsh, too real, too stupid, too much. As we got within eyeshot of the bar, Annie and I both clocked Danielle outside.

"Oh no," was our standard, in-unison response. She was seated with a few others and I expected she was showing off her engagement ring. Charlie was standing there too, looking strangely uninvolved, a little apart from the group as he often was, listening to somebody on his mobile. Mercifully he had his back turned to the street, allowing Annie and me to carry on walking swiftly by, undetected. There was no way I was gatecrashing the 'party'.

Two doors down was another bar. It wasn't our favourite place to go but it was a safe haven. As we turned in the door of the other bar I was aware that Charlie quite likely could see from the periphery of Cafe Noir, as his face had been turned in that direction. I felt my soul squeeze up in tension. I didn't even glance up to see. I was too scared to make eye contact, worried I might either burst into tears or be tempted to slap him across the face, or both. We got inside, ordered drinks and sat ourselves down. A horrible realisation occurred to me. I was going to keep seeing him. I was going to have to keep witnessing him. He was going to keep cropping up. For as long as I lived around the area, this was going to keep happening. This felt unfair, and I thought about how I was going to cope with that. I don't remember what Annie and I talked about. I felt uncomfortable, and try as I might, it was hard to settle and relax.

We'd probably been there for about twenty minutes before we saw a sight I couldn't quite believe. It felt more like a dream than a real occurrence, but we both saw it. Charlie came strolling down the street from Cafe Noir on his own. Outside the bar we were in, we saw him stare searchingly through the windows, like he was trying to spot me. I couldn't believe how blatant it looked. This was crazy! He'd just got engaged and he was walking round looking for me. OK, I knew I could be wrong but I couldn't figure out why else he'd be peering in the window like that, knowing (I assumed) we'd entered this bar. He then floated on by and I'm not sure what he did after that, because I was speechless and turned from the window to avoid seeing any more.

"What's he doing? What's he playing at?" was my general perplexed reaction. It wasn't something Annie could answer and I didn't expect her to. We made a point of taking a different route home because I didn't want to walk back past the "charade", as I referred to it, outside Cafe Noir. I would have preferred not to have seen him, let alone see him looking haunted and sad and lost like he had looked. This wasn't the behaviour of a recently engaged and happy man.

I made an appointment to speak with Zharha. I had a hundred and one things to say to her but at the end of the day all my incomprehension boiled down to "Why?", "How?" and "What now?" I thought back to the severe and prolonged headache I'd had the week before this news. Something told me it was connected. On some level it was as though my body had psychically obtained the news before my conscious mind did and knew the magnitude of what had occurred. Once again I found myself walking along the King's Road to see my dear mentor.

We sat in her office and I told Zharha about the voice that spoke to me on the way to Hudson's Cave, delivering the horrible news in that neutral, factual but absolutely accurate style. Zharha listened intently, sadly stirring her coffee, then explained it was my guides and that they wanted to prepare me. I agreed, and added that even with their warning I was still gobsmacked but it would have been an even greater shock without that precognitive buffering. I'd heard messages before, discerned information before from thin air, but this was the clearest I'd ever heard them deliver a message and the quickest it was ever proven to be correct. It was interesting because part of me expected guides to talk dramatically in proclamations, for smoke and fireworks to burst forth, for thunder and lightning and earthquakes to rumble as a voice boomed out across the land, like in the Bible. This was far more subtle and personal. Over time I came to recognise them when they spoke, though they didn't speak to me often in this manner.

Zharha and I also discussed the strange synchronicity involving Charlie performing in Edinburgh the night Annie and I would be arriving there, which was now in three weeks' time. Though the coincidence had excited me when I first discovered it, right now I didn't even want to go. With sadness I realised that cutting off from Charlie would mean cutting off from some other things that involved him. I still didn't want to see Charlie and sure as hell didn't want to hear him acting out scenes about love and passion, because fittingly or not, the production he was starring in was called *Lights, Camera, Love Action*.

Talking to Zharha, as ever, was a help. She agreed getting married was not what Charlie wanted.

"It's his miserable life and why anyone *wants* to be miserable I will never understand. But he has chosen to stick his head in the sand like an ostrich," she told me. She explained to me that I had no choice but to really let go. "At the end of the day, you aren't going to love a married man no matter who it is or how unmarried he really is in his head."

I could only agree, maddening though it was. Even though, buried beneath all the pain and upset, I knew I still loved him – the real him. And that was the peculiar thing. The person who was doing these recent things didn't *seem* like Charlie. He had the air of an imposter. It was as though he'd wandered so far off his path he was becoming somebody else.

I also mentioned the near-close encounter outside Cafe Noir the other night to Zharha. She shook her head, saying, "Yeah, he was looking for you. He's *always* looking for you, just to glimpse you – but then what, after that, when he finds you? That's the problem!" It was indeed. It summed up a dance we'd been doing for years and maybe that's all it would ever be. "It's confirmation of his feelings, sure, but we need realism. Confirmation of feelings, of a connection means nothing in his world of self-sabotage. At this point, he's dug himself a hole. He won't risk the confrontation of breaking it off. *Why*? I still scratch my head…" It was hard to hear these things but I knew she was right. I really had no choice but to turn away, to leave him to it.

So this is what I attempted to do. Zharha had also explained that what was making it so hard for me to let go was that Charlie had some of my 'soul parts'. This I understood as little pieces of me that I had given him, fragments that kept us connected. I had pieces of his soul too, which she said I'd been reluctant to return, though I had recently done so. She wanted me to ask him for my soul parts back as this was the only way I'd be able to move on and love another. How to do that? It wasn't something I could do in person. I couldn't send him an invoice or a demand for their return. I just had to ask him spiritually, through meditation.

I agreed this was something that felt necessary. Something was keeping me tied to him. So, I gave it a go. It was always easy to speak to Charlie in this mode. I only had to close my eyes and he'd readily appear. He always seemed close by. In some ways he always *was* close by. This was part of the problem. Much of the beauty and difficulty of our connection came from its all-encompassing multidimensionality. You couldn't close it off, put it in the cupboard, or screw the lid down. Or you could, but it would be lying beside you on the pillow when you climbed into bed, hanging outside the front door when you left the house in the morning, lurking in the corner of the lift as you pressed the buttons to the second floor. It was like a mist that could curl under doors and into the deepest crevices of your being. Our souls were enmeshed and they didn't want to separate. That was all very well if two people were physically together – whether friends or lovers – but right now we didn't feel like either. What were we to one another? Shadows of each other? Reflections of each other? Part and parcel of one another?

I didn't know what the answer was, only that whatever it was, this was very precious and for that reason it somehow didn't feel right to try and cut it off. Yet, how could I go on when he was choosing a life that didn't involve me? It seemed unfair to be so glued together at soul level when the physical world appeared to be pulling us apart. Or was this all my head? Was I really so connected to him or was this some form of delusion or insanity? There were very few people I could talk to about this, other than Zharha and Annie and my sisters, with whom I'd shared much of it.

And what about Charlie? Who did *he* talk to about this? Perhaps Jay? Perhaps not. I couldn't see him phoning up a psychic or healer like I did. I couldn't see him talking to anyone about it. Perhaps he did in his sleep? Perhaps that's why Danielle was so angry and threatened. Perhaps he *didn't* experience it like I did. But even as I put forward that suggestion every fibre of my being told me, *He does! But he must have some way of blocking it, shoving it back down*, I argued with myself. *Otherwise how could he live the life he does, with another woman?* As usual, when I had these conversations with myself I gave up in befuddlement. I couldn't explain what I was going through or why, so to try to see it through his eyes was not going to work. I could only summarise that it just was the way it was and I had to find ways of being OK with that and getting on with life. Getting on with life! That was the thing: when your whole understanding and perspective on what life is has been called into question, getting on with it is something that requires major adjustment. Getting on with what? Why was I here? What was all this trying to show me? I knew there was more to the whole cosmic wheel than I'd previously imagined. Or perhaps the truth was it *was* how I imagined; my imaginings weren't fantasy. Life is not as we know it.

I did try asking Charlie for my soul parts back (telepathically). He didn't want to give them and to be honest I'm not sure how much I fully wanted to take them, because even though I agreed with Zharha that I needed to be whole and complete to move on, some intrinsic part of me just didn't want to sever this thing. Indeed, I felt some guilt for even trying. But oh, how I wanted to be happy. That was important to me and right now, Charlie wasn't making me happy. Of course, what I needed to learn, and was learning in a cack-handed manner, was that nobody can *make* anybody happy and it's not their duty to. We are responsible for our own happiness. It doesn't come from the outside. I knew that but on some level I was still looking to him as a source of happiness. There was still this persistent notion that Charlie was the key to my well-being and happiness. This was a notion I had to get rid of, and the faster the better. I was getting there but there were a lot of tears and torment to plod through, a lot of banging my head against the concrete wall before I realised it was all up to me.

It was all up to me.

Thirty - One

I talked to Zharha quite a bit during the next month. We covered a lot of ground but it felt as though the ground kept moving, like shifting sand in the desert. She had advised me to tell Charlie how I felt about his choice, to get it off my chest, to help release it and bring me closer to being able to walk away. Walking away was still my aim but it was important to do it with a clear conscience and no regrets. I couldn't see an opportunity presenting itself easily for me to speak to Charlie about things – or whether it was even the right thing to do. I tried articulating my hurt feelings in a letter to him. Even if I didn't give it to him, it seemed a useful therapeutic activity. When it was written, with much editing and uncertainty, I wondered if it *was* a good idea to hand it over to him or not? The letter was both a testament of my love, a lament of the loss of my dream and a mild rant about him seeming to have strayed off course and not being much of a friend. It was the final part that I was unsure about saying. I worried I was being too judgemental and too harsh. Yet, in so many ways he *was* behaving out of character and had been for some time. It felt like he needed a wake-up call and for some reason I felt almost duty-bound to deliver it – yet, simultaneously I felt I had no right to be so direct. Who was I to point out my perception of the error of his choices? Who *was* I?

"If not, you, who?" Zharha asked squarely, when we next spoke and I made panic-filled protests about spelling it out to Charlie. I thought about her question. I had this feeling that nobody around Charlie was telling it like it was, and I finally agreed with Zharha that I had to speak my truth. I worried about his potential response. Of course I did. I had to be prepared for him to never speak to me again. He may think I had no right to pour out my feelings, to tell him in no uncertain terms about how much this had impacted on my life, how my dreams were crushed by his choice as no matter what he had or hadn't said in recent months, I'd still held that hope in my heart, that stubborn hope that we had a chance. It now felt like I was being forced to excavate that hope from my heart-shaped chamber. The bulldozers were lined up in the street; the cranes were looming overhead. This engagement and impending wedding cast the kind of shadow I could not ignore. He was turning his back on me and though he had every right to, I did feel he ought to know where that left me and that this changed everything.

I had to walk away simply because I couldn't bear the pain of watching. If hope had to be extinguished then I couldn't go on seeing him and just pretending everything was OK. If he wasn't going to be my man, I had to heal my heart so either another man could be – or at least I could be free and at peace, healed and happy on my own. That was something we all should strive to attain. If we all could be whole and healed alone, all relationships would come from a place of love – love doesn't need, love simply is. Unconditional love asks for nothing, needs nothing, is everything – but it starts with loving yourself unconditionally and that's no easy feat. Yet, I knew that was what I had to learn – to love not just myself, but everyone unconditionally. What I also only half-knew was that this was the path to true happiness.

So, I had this letter to give Charlie. I carried it around in my handbag. It sat in an airmail envelope I'd stolen from the stationary cupboard at work. My sense of humour must have still been intact on some level because I thought the airmail envelope signified lightness and speed, whereas the one-page letter was heavy as a brick and it certainly didn't leave my hands in a speedy manner, much as I wanted it to. Despite me worrying that Charlie was going to crop up everywhere I looked recently, he was suddenly strikingly absent from the usual haunts where we'd encounter each other. Each time I went out to a local bar or cafe the letter came with me, weighing down my being like a ball and chain. Why couldn't he just turn up and let me give it to him? Why?

During this time I remember a strange happening on the bus coming home from work. I asked for a sign to help lead me in the right direction, to tell me what I needed to know. The very next moment the woman sitting in front of me on the bus pulled a book out of her bag and opened it. I could see very clearly over her shoulder, and to my surprise I soon saw the book contained a character called Charlie. She turned the page onto a chapter called *The Wedding* – the first line stated, *It was a sad wedding.* I averted my eyes uncomfortably, a surge of shock shooting through my veins. I asked for a sign. I got one, instantly... but what was I supposed to make of that? I guess I just needed to deliver that letter and walk away as I was planning. I knew there *was* something sad about this wedding, something sad and strange, and that sensation went beyond the impact it had on me.

Perhaps the good thing about the delay with finding an opportunity to give Charlie the letter was that it gave me a chance to make sure the letter was truly what I wanted to say and that I truly wanted to give it to him, because I was very aware that once the deed was done there was no going back. I had to walk away. I didn't *want* to walk away but I considered it the only healthy option. It was never written to try and make him change his mind. It wasn't a plea for anything other than that he understand that I'd reached the end of a road and needed to move on, and for him to respect that and not play games with me. And yes, I did want to let him know this had hurt but that I refused to let myself be continually hurt by watching it. I did feel he'd let me down as a friend. I knew what was between us was more complicated than straightforward friendship. Whether he was willing to admit it or not there were other feelings in the mix on both sides, so in many ways I understood why we didn't have a 'normal' friendship, but in recent times I did feel he'd just not treated me well. He'd withdrawn rather than be honest with me, he'd not answered calls, he gave the impression he wasn't worried if I was in his life or not. For someone who'd told me he'd be the best friend I could ever have, it was understandable I felt let down.

Perhaps the engagement news was the catalyst needed to make me do what perhaps I should have done before: cut ties and walk away if he couldn't – for whatever reason – face the music with me, acknowledge this incredible even if at times downright terrifying energy that was between us. If he couldn't explore it, open to it, honour or embrace it I had to figure out what to do on my own. A terrible shame, a tragedy not to be able to walk through this life together, the way I felt we were supposed to, but at this point in time, we clearly weren't on the same page of the beautiful book we'd been writing and I needed to fast-forward to the index to see if I could find a way to understand where I should be. What I found in that index was helpful but I noticed the page numbers were either absent or kept changing… the concepts, the lessons, the karma, the purpose, the magnificence of our love were all there but the how and the when and the ifs – the notions of linear time and the rigidity of the three-dimensional world couldn't be applied. I could never organise this story in a framework that could be easily followed, predicted or intellectually understood. It couldn't be grasped or held on to. It could only be sensed and stared at in absolute awe, understood and accepted in surrender mode. I still had a lot of learning ahead of me and my soul knew it and was guiding me away from the man I couldn't bear to be without, so I could learn to be with myself fully and completely, learn to be myself with no apologies… and maybe so that he could too.

Thirty - Two

August was over halfway through and the date had rolled round for Annie and me to catch our train and attend the last week of the Edinburgh Festival. When I packed my case with a strange mix of summery and autumnal clothes to try and cater for the unpredictable, mixed-up weather we were experiencing, I also packed the by now creased airmail envelope containing the letter. Charlie hadn't showed up prior to our departure and so the short epistle had to accompany me. I prayed it wouldn't come back with me. It had to be delivered and hopefully, somehow, I could get it to him at the play that night. We didn't have tickets for the play. It was sold out and my heart couldn't handle the actor killing me softly with his words so I didn't want to attend anyway.

Annie and I agreed that we'd check into our hotel, then head to the venue where the play was being performed and hope that fate would give me an opportunity to run into Charlie. The train journey was an odd mixture of silly giggles and inward tension. I was glad to be going on holiday. I needed a change of scene. Balham had been feeling claustrophobic and oppressive as everywhere I went reminded me of Charlie. I'd never visited Edinburgh, so with a courageous heart I boarded the train. I was in training to hope for new things. I looked forward to getting immersed in the festival and new scenery. I stared out the train window at the rolling green Scottish countryside canopied by a brooding, pregnant sky. These heavy skies seemed to have become a regular backdrop at the moment. I could just chuck the letter out the window. I could just tear it up. I could, but I couldn't. It felt that if I didn't part with it the pain would never leave and I could never get out of this odd limbo. So, I must do the deed. I must be brave. I worried I wouldn't get the chance. I worried I would get the chance. I was worried sick by time we approached Edinburgh but still had every intention of going through with it.

Here we were. Edinburgh Waverley. We weaved our way through the crowds and jumped in a taxi. Neither of us knew where the hotel was or we probably would have tried to find our way on foot. I'd always been an on-foot kind of person. The taxi driver chatted jovially and had some banter with Annie about football. I was half-tuned in and half-tuned out. I wondered if I was making the biggest mistake of my life. The crowded streets of Edinburgh swished by and I stared, glazed and worried. Yet as soon as I considered retracting the letter I quickly reminded myself that he'd left me little choice. If I didn't walk away, as I put it, I couldn't make a fresh start. I suppose I was viewing marriage as being for life even though a little voice in my head was telling me that wouldn't be the case here and wasn't the case in many cases. Still, whatever the future held, I had to pull away and nurse my soul back to health. It felt vital.

We were there. There stood our hotel for the week. After a brief flurry of delight at discovering our adjacent rooms and a quick trip to a nearby cafe to grab a slice of takeaway pizza, the reality of handing over that letter was getting all too real and my entire being was inwardly jittering. The pizza was wholesome and tasty but I wolfed it down without really tasting it, which was definitely not my normal style. I tended to eat slowly, to savour each bite, but I was in a tormented tizzy. The worry I was making a big mistake kept surfacing but I kept questioning it, asking what the alternative was. I felt the need to go within and be sure, so I took a few minutes alone, placing my hand on the letter, silently praying to the powers that be that it would go exactly where it needed to go, wherever that may be.

"OK," I announced to Annie after freshening up my make-up, "I'm ready!" Annie knew roughly where the venue was as she'd visited it before but it was all new to me... except it wasn't. The streets felt oddly familiar and the landscape kept hitting me like long-forgotten paintings, rearing out of the ground, coming above surface – yet they were memories I could barely decipher. Maybe I dreamt of these streets. Maybe I walked them before? Maybe this all happened before and was happening again – yet I felt I was somehow breaking the mould; that this time it was going to be different. I was trying so hard to do what I felt was the right thing. There was a sense that I was attempting to straighten out an ancient pattern that had been caught in an endless cycle of repeat play for centuries, as if I was trying to stop that cycle of pain, to balance some age-old karma. I didn't understand the feeling but it was there and somehow I trusted that the right thing would happen.

We walked the crowded streets of Edinburgh towards The Coal-Shed venue where the play was taking place. It was around six o'clock, the time of day any rehearsals would usually have happened and there was no real reason to think Charlie would be hanging around the venue, but without really thinking about it I just kind of supposed that if Charlie was meant to receive this letter he'd make an appearance somewhere on the streets of Edinburgh, and heading for the venue seemed as good a place as any to navigate towards. Within ten minutes we were nearing the vicinity of the theatre. Annie said it was just a couple of minutes away and a feeling of panic attacked me. I was suddenly utterly petrified and thought, *I can't do this!* I was just about to turn to Annie and say, "Let's go back!" but before the words could even rise up my throat it was too late. Charlie was coming. There he was. We had come to a standstill on the corner and he was walking right towards us. When he clocked us he slowed down and then ground to a halt in front of us, his mouth literally falling slightly open in surprise, and pointing at us as though to express how out of context we must have seemed at that moment for him.

I knew then I had to do the deed. He had showed up and on his own, and here was the perfect opportunity to hand over the crumpled airmail envelope that sat in my handbag. We started to speak. I explained we were here on holiday, which was absolutely true but I didn't expect him to believe it and it didn't really matter whether he did or not. He said the performance was sold out but that he'd see what he could do. He might be able to squeeze us in somehow. Though I heard his words and knew he would have managed it and it would have been the normal thing for us all to do in the past, I also knew this wasn't a normal situation. Part of me knew, too, that this might be the last time I saw him, the last time we spoke as friends, depending on how he took my letter, if he'd even read it. He also said he was going to meet with his mother, who happened to be in town with a friend for the festival too. I immediately felt bad when I heard this as I didn't want my letter to spoil his evening or interfere with his meeting with his mother, but at the same time I knew I had to deliver it. I could feel the tension like a sustained drum roll that couldn't wait much longer – and it was now or never.

Annie said she needed to go the cashpoint and Charlie jumped in quickly with instructions on where cashpoints were. He'd performed here quite a few times over the years and seemed to know the area well. Annie was kindly trying to give us a little privacy, but the traffic had other ideas and I could feel her straining to escape but being held nearby as I plunged my hand into my bag, saying something daft like, "I've got something I want to give you."

I have to give Charlie credit for appearing quite normal about this. He didn't seem to look particularly puzzled or worried about me diving into my bag and producing an envelope, but perhaps he was just in a general state of shock that this encounter was even happening in the first place, and so even if I'd produced a miniature unicorn he may not have batted an eyelid.

"It's something I'd like you to read," I continued as the envelope passed from my hands to his.

"I will," he said in a strangely dutiful manner, and tucked the envelope inside his jacket, close to his heart. I couldn't help noticing that, and it felt deeply symbolic. My heart was broken and I felt like I was somehow breaking his in return, even though my intention was nothing of the sort. I thought I was doing the right thing. I hoped I was. After the letter had been delivered I think Charlie was becoming increasingly aware that something weird was in the mix and neither of us lingered. I wanted to get the hell out of there, as I'm very sure both Annie and Charlie did. We said our goodbyes with some half-hearted mention of maybe getting to the play later but I think we all knew that wasn't going to happen.

Charlie moved on towards the Royal Mile and Annie and I started walking quickly back onto Market Street. I felt the need to walk fast and keep moving. I felt quivery and strange. We talked rapidly, both struck by the uncanny way he'd shown up on his own, creating the perfect opportunity for the letter to be delivered. I couldn't have asked for a better opportunity, odd as it had felt to be standing on the corner, saying those words and giving him my broken-hearted decision to walk away. It made me feel it *must* be the right thing to do. It had to be. Yet, a little panicky voice inside wondered if I meant it? Could I walk away from someone who meant the world to me? But what else could I do if he was marrying someone else? There was no plausible, healthy alternative. He hadn't even told me he loved me. He hadn't really told me anything. No matter how much I sensed it, knew it, felt it, saw it – he hadn't told me and his actions were telling me something else, so therefore… walk away.

Now I was going to have to figure out *how* to do it. How? We'd walked by now through the Grassmarket and it was starting to drizzle slightly so we entered a bar and each ordered a glass of red wine. We climbed on high stools and watched the Scottish mist coming down outside, filling the air with mystery and drama. I clung to that glass of wine like some life support system. What had I done? Why did this feel so momentous? The worry I'd upset him greatly was already surfacing but I tried to hold it back down. This really had to be done. I couldn't just say nothing – or could I have? He, after all, was very good at saying nothing. Perhaps I said too much? Perhaps not enough? Perhaps I was just analysing it all too much as I was prone to do. Annie and I noticed a poster on the window of the bar advertising the performance happening that night that was going on in The Coal-Shed. There was his name in a curling, red lettering. My soul gulped. Would I ever see him perform again? Would I ever hear Charlie's voice again? I steered my mind away from these thoughts as best I could and attempted to concentrate more on the sense of relief I felt for finally getting that letter out of my hands. I did feel relief. It was a big deal and it was done. But I was slightly troubled by the persistence of a feeling of unfinished business, despite the initial release. I realised I was waiting for some kind of reaction from him, and I really had no idea what that would be.

When we'd finished the wine the drizzle had stopped and Annie and I went strolling about the streets of Edinburgh, ending up in a lovely little cafe that looked about to close but when we stepped inside with hopeful eyes we were invited to sit down, which we did happily whilst the coffee machine made comforting hissing sounds behind us. I was keeping my chin up nicely but I felt exhausted and unsure if what I had done was right or wrong. At any rate, I'd done it so there was no point having any regrets. It's not like I hadn't thought it through. We looked through a festival brochure and made some potential plans for the week. I had to look ahead like this. I knew I had to stop looking back. Thank goodness there were no more Charlie-related posters in this cafe. The rest of my life, a life without Charlie, was in front of me. I wished I felt more enthusiastic about that but I also knew I needed to give myself time.

Thirty - Three

Back at the hotel, we went to bed quite early. We were both tired and I didn't really want to sit up as I was trying not to dwell on the letter business. I climbed into what would be my bed for the next week and lay listening to the nocturnal noises of the city. It was still relatively early, just gone half past ten, and the festival-goers were still coming and going out on the street. I expected Charlie's performance was over. I felt bad for him having to perform after reading that letter. I had visions of him being upset and angry but not telling a soul, not even Jay, who I suspected might also be in town as his name was mentioned on the poster also. But then again, I could be completely wrong. It may not upset him. He may even be relieved I was moving on, or attempting to. But even if he was, he would surely not like the accusations of him not being a good friend and my implication that getting married wasn't what I felt he really wanted to do. They were not easily digestible comments even if they were true – and were they? Well, he hadn't been a good friend to me of late, I reminded myself. He had in the past but this had been a complicated and uneasy relationship for some time now. What we meant to each other defied any normal category. I knew I wasn't imagining what was there but what I was finally accepting was that even if Charlie did feel things for me, he wasn't doing anything about those feelings. He was moving in the opposite direction for whatever reason.

I hoped I'd get to sleep but after an hour I realised it wasn't going to happen easily, if at all. I found myself checking my phone that lay silently on the pillow beside me. Even though I wasn't expecting him to call I had to consider it was a possibility. I pictured him furious and accusing me of making outrageous judgements and assumptions – even though deep, deep down I didn't think he'd actually disagree with me. Still, most probably he wouldn't appreciate me pointing these things out to him. Who would? Sleep was eluding me. The night went on and I tossed and turned and ended up just waiting for dawn to break so I could at least get out and about and change the scenery.

It wasn't easy to say goodbye and if this was the only way, wasn't there a better way of doing the 'only way' than this? I didn't want to lose him but in so many ways I didn't have him to lose, so whatever I was losing was perhaps already lost. Was it ever there at all? My thoughts were becoming less and less rational but I couldn't find a way to turn them off. *So, it's all over now,* I told myself. I cried quietly and looked at the unfamiliar furniture around me in the small hotel room. I was going to have to get over this. Somehow. I was going to have to say goodbye to the familiar furniture and get used to new shapes. I had a week in Edinburgh that I was determined to enjoy. I had to keep actively switching focus as he still kept occupying my headspace. The delivery of the letter was supposed to be my liberation, but that liberation felt half-hearted.

I couldn't claim to feel free. I hadn't put down the load, though I had maybe put down a couple of parcels. Though I tried very hard to rid my being of the past and the pain, I didn't quite know how to shed it all. It was still there, trailing after me silently as I walked through the streets of Edinburgh for the rest of the week, waving at me vacantly from the roof of the castle, hovering on the corner where I'd delivered the letter, which I passed several times more during my stay. *Charlie. Charlie. Charlie.* He was just as much in my head as ever.

Charlie didn't call in the morning – or the next day, or during the week, or the week after when back in London – and it was clear to me that he was going to say nothing. A big, deep, wide, long, deafening nothing. In truth, that was what I expected him to do all along, though it was impossible to completely quell those hopes that fluttered around my heart. The hope he might call me up or come round and tell me he loved me really and that he didn't want me to walk away, that he'd called off the engagement and he wanted to be with me. Those hopes faded quickly and I was left feeling exasperated with myself. Why couldn't I be done with this? What the hell was wrong with me?

Yet, I was getting somewhere. I was facing things. Our disconnection just wasn't going to happen overnight. I felt him energetically like I always had done and this was part of the problem. It was never a case of out of sight and out of mind with Charlie. I turned to Zharha on my return from Edinburgh and luckily she had a lot of time, patience and good advice for me. So, I worked on releasing him and ignoring him when I felt that pull in the night. It wasn't easy and it didn't come naturally to me. I still felt a ridiculous amount of guilt about what felt like turning my back on him – but it simply had to be done. Gradually I felt I was making progress and the pulling seemed to lessen. I wasn't sure if that was because he was doing it less or I was hearing it less (or both), but I felt him as a distant swish at arm's length, rather than roaring, in-your-face traffic. I had hopes I would soon be back to my old self, back to the Eileen I was before I'd ever met him. Even though I felt I could never be the same after this experience, I tried to trust I could.

However, being the person I was before I met him – or the person I thought I was – wasn't the answer. This whole thing had happened to change that person and it took another major exfoliation of the soul for me to see that. It was about dealing with those core issues that were shoved away earlier in life and maybe in other incarnations. When previous love relationships – or friendships – had broken up I'd suffer for a while and then somehow be OK again without really dealing with all those thorns in my heart, all those gashes and bumps. There was something about this thing with Charlie that demanded I did deal with it. It just wouldn't let go if I wouldn't learn the lessons. I wasn't addressing the root issues that were part of my psyche before Charlie ever showed up. Those wounds were already there. He just happened to trigger them in a dramatic way. He never deliberately rubbed salt in them, he was far too kind and considerate to do that, but the salt of my tears, provoked by how things had gone down with the man I considered the love of my life, fell in each and every one of those emotional wounds until they became red and inflamed. I had to heal those wounds. I had to face them and stop pretending I didn't have them. And sad to say, it took me a while to fully grasp that. I thought letting go of Charlie was all I needed to do. It wasn't. The real work had perhaps only just begun, and even though over the next year or so I appeared to be falling apart worse than ever, I was actually hitting the rock bottom I had to hit to scare myself enough that I would save myself and learn that I was the only person I could save, and that I could and would be saved.

Back in London, I landed straight back into my previous life and the wheel kept on turning. I attempted to keep busy and keep Charlie out of my mind but in truth he was still very much there and I felt shaky and full of questions, not in the state of closure I'd hoped for. I'd only been back a few days when we had one of our near-meetings. I was waiting for a lift from Wendy on the intersection of a two roads a stone's throw from Hudson's Cave. As I waited I felt a pull in a particular direction towards Bedford Hill, yet at the same time as I felt this pull, I also felt what I can only describe as an invisible hand on my shoulder asking me to stay put. I resisted the pull but felt agitated about it. Was it Charlie? Or was I just imagining it? Wendy and her partner Sandy swung round the bend, waving cheerfully, and I catapulted myself forward to jump into their smiling car. Within minutes, I gasped quietly to myself as we shot down Bedford Hill and I spotted Charlie and Danielle standing outside Cafe Noir. From that brief glimpse all I sensed was heaviness and despondency from the two of them. Wendy's car whisked me away and I saw no more.

For the next six months this was all I saw of Charlie – fleeting, long-distance snapshots from moving vehicles. It was normally me that was in the vehicle and he'd be standing on a corner or perhaps walking down the street. I once saw him standing on a traffic island near Euston while I sat on the upper deck of a bus. Each time this would happen, with perhaps one or two exceptions, I'd have an inner alert, a knowing that he was about to manifest. I'd see him and not know if he saw me, expecting he wouldn't, and I'd feel my heart pounding the way it always had when he came into view. I wondered why this was happening. It was as though we were still gravitating towards each other, yet paradoxically being kept at arm's length at the same time, a feeling akin to 'You can glimpse but you can't touch' as well as that old adage 'You can run but you can't hide' – but who was orchestrating these glimpses and near misses? Who decided to make it happen or not happen? Were we puppets or guided souls?

Looking back now, I see those fleeting physical intersections of our souls in time and place as signals that the connection was still alive. Those ethereal neural pathways were still functional, still firing, still fizzling. We were like branches on trees separated by a big, fat wall. We could still brush each other with our leaves in the quiet of the night when the wind blew in the right direction but beneath the soil, our roots were all wrapped up together, though this was the part no one could logically see. That didn't mean the roots weren't there, hugging, nourishing, growing. He wasn't really as 'gone' as he appeared to be on the physical plane. He wasn't really gone energetically at all, and this was something I'd grapple with for a long time, feeling he ought to either be there or not be there, one or the other, missing the point that a spiritual bond like this can't be done away with like something physical can. It wasn't a question of cutting it off, stamping on it, trying to force shut the lid that would inevitably come undone when the energy so desired. It was more a question of acceptance. The Universe had brought us together, torn us apart and now it felt as though we were going to have to live apart, at least for now, but not without these timely reminders that seemed to say, despite the surface view, our paths were still somehow entwined.

Still, the glaring truth was that right here, right now, I had to forge out a path for myself that didn't involve him. This was vital for my soul, for my growth, and slowly this was becoming apparent to me. Though I didn't fully understand the mechanics of the Universe there was a feeling deep down that it knew what it was doing, even if I didn't, even if Charlie didn't, even if most of us don't. One way or another, the Universe is determined that we do what is required for us to be who we're meant to be. It just had to keep whacking me over the head for a bit longer until I stopped fighting it and surrendered fully to its wonder and wisdom. At this point, I still wasn't there but I had split-second moments of knowing it would all be alright and this was all meant to happen for a million and one reasons.

I was still working at *South of the River* and as it was the close of a decade I was working on an article featuring the best performers and performances of the last ten years. Needless to say, I wanted to feature the Last Exit Players. They'd been featured in the magazine frequently and it would be expected that they would be included in a retrospective of the decade, even though they were no longer together. I contacted each of the group for a comment. Though I found the task daunting, that included Charlie, as he was so often the spokesperson for the group. It was no surprise that he didn't respond to my request, which I'd tried to make sound as unemotional and normal as possible. This upset me more than I'd bargained for. I hoped he'd come round and was just having a sulk, but he didn't get back to me and the rest of the group were making embarrassed noises about him, joking and implying he was an awkward bugger. I probably shouldn't even have tried but a part of me yearned for contact, for the knowledge that I hadn't completely blown it, and that we might ever speak again. It was frustrating to feel this way when I'd been aiming to feel the opposite. My head wanted to turn my back but my soul wanted the complete opposite.

The more time passed, the more I missed seeing him, even though I'd truly not wanted to see him after the engagement news and at that point I'd completely meant it. I worried that he was furious. I worried that he thought I was crazy and delusional. I worried that he'd cut me out of his life and heart (if I'd ever even been there at all) and had forgotten all about me. If he could do it, why couldn't I? *It's supposed to be over*, I told myself. *Why are you still thinking about him? Why do you expect him to return your call when you said you were walking away? Hmm?* I beat myself up, as usual. He kept quiet, as usual.

I ran the feature in the magazine, managing to thinly paper over the pain I felt whilst penning those words, managing to sound celebratory rather than transfer the forlorn feeling that sat in my lap with my laptop as the words filled the screen. It was almost Christmas and twinkling lights appeared all over Balham, beckoning me to be joyful – but somehow they only increased my wistfulness. I hid it as much as I could and sometimes I did feel fine, but I couldn't fill the void Charlie had left in my life at this point. I didn't know how to fill it, or if it was even possible. I'd have given anything to sit with him and clink glasses and feel the warmth we used to share come rushing back, the warmth, the thrill, the love. It was still in my heart no matter what. I was still looking for external answers and solutions. I still doubted the wisdom of the Universe, even though it had performed amazing feats right before my eyes. I still hadn't walked through that inner door and hugged my soul instead of wanting to hug him. The healing process was quietly happening, though, and it was up to me how much I resisted.

Thirty-Four

After Christmas that year I had word from Jay that there was a play in production that he had stage-designed and that Charlie was performing in. Jay and I were still in touch and indeed Jay seemed to feel badly about Charlie's silence and whatever awkward business had happened between us. I didn't discuss it. I had no idea how much Jay knew. It was quite possible that Charlie hadn't said a word to him – yet on some level, I could tell he knew something was up. Perhaps he just thought I was upset about the engagement. The wedding was yet to happen. I didn't mention it and nor did Jay. I felt it looming ahead, though, and part of me wished he'd just get on with it, while the other part of me hoped he'd somehow change his mind. It still felt like a raw wound, despite my letter and my feeble attempts to kiss it all goodbye.

I agonised about whether to go to this play. Normally I always caught Charlie's performances when they were happening locally if I was about. It always had been the natural thing to do, and there'd been some really good times around many of these events. For the first time, I had to reconsider. How would it feel to see him now? Would it stir everything up again? Not that things had exactly settled down for me, but it was more chronic than acute pain at this point and I didn't want another dose of the acute, gut-wrenching variety. What bothered me was the level of fear I felt around the situation. I was scared to see him and I could barely explain why. Scared he would ignore me? Scared he would act like nothing had happened? Scared he would be wearing an engagement ring and somehow just not be the man I knew? It was all these things and more. That fear, that crazy energy had surfaced many times before in our encounters but usually when things had been good between us it translated into excitement and just pure, beautiful love. It felt as though this love had somehow been tainted, left out in the rain with all the colours running and blurring. It was too sad a sight to see, but was averting my eyes just cowardly or was it the sane thing to do?

I decided to go to see the play. I wasn't going to let fear get the better of me. I'd face the music as I'd always done and after all, I didn't want to let my situation with Charlie affect my relationship with Jay, who seemed to want me to come. I worried I was contradicting myself with my 'walking away' mantra but as time went on, I realised what I was attempting to walk away from was the pain, not Charlie himself – and learning that the source of the pain was something inside me, and where he was and what he did was a trigger rather than the root. I wanted to be in a position where I could see him and feel completely OK. At that moment it was still unthinkable – and thinking too much was fuelling the unthinkable. For the nights leading up to this gig and the prospect of seeing him I developed a horrible insomnia. It became so relentless I even visited the doctor and asked apologetically for some sleeping tablets. I was having a stressful time, I explained, and pretended it was relating to an impending job interview. I couldn't confess that it was a reaction to what had happened with some guy who I wasn't even in a relationship with. The medical profession would class me as a nutter. For the first time in my life, the night before the play, I slipped a sleeping pill into my mouth and the sweet oblivion I was seeking was mine – for a short time.

So that evening in late January, Annie and I stepped out into the city, heading for a pub with an upstairs theatre in the East End where the play was running. I'd been there a couple of times before and it wasn't my favourite venue. It had a big, empty feeling inside of it even when fully populated. As we drew near the pub, my legs turned to jelly and I felt sick. I considered going home again, but having come this far it felt important to proceed. My anxiety was obviously rubbing off on Annie, who admitted to feeling strangely tense too. We entered the pub and bolted straight into the toilets in the basement, where somehow I managed to pull myself together and then Annie and I crept back upstairs into the bar. There were two plays on the bill that night but the place wasn't busy. As we entered the main downstairs bar, I was aware of a group of local guys from our part of town leaning on the counter by the fruit machines. One was Keith, a close friend of Charlie's. He said hello, giving me the curious, intrigued look many of his friends tended to give me. I said hello and kept walking, feeling unsteady and wanting to find a quiet corner. I made a beeline for a distant corner I could spy, feeling like I was walking through a sea of snakes, whilst Annie walked alongside me.

When we were approaching my destined corner,

Annie said in a surprised whisper, "Did you know you just walked by Charlie?"

I was shocked. "You're joking!"

"No, he's over there with Johnny and Keith," Annie told me. I was stunned that I could possibly have walked straight past Charlie without noticing him.

I looked warily in the direction Annie had indicated and despite pillars and people getting in the way, I clocked the man himself. There was Charlie hovering about with a small group of people, most of whom I knew at least vaguely. He seemed to be deliberately cultivating an air of nonchalance, which I guessed was partly because he was due to get onstage at any point, but I also couldn't help thinking it was for my benefit. I sensed he wanted me to see that he was doing fine, that he wasn't worried about an encounter with me, that he was just going about his business as usual. Yet, this didn't feel like business as usual as Charlie didn't normally hang around publically before performances, or certainly not in recent times. The other unusual factor was that Danielle wasn't in the group. I expected she must be somewhere in the house though, as it was another unthinkable thought that she wouldn't be. I glanced at Charlie a little, though I didn't allow myself to look in depth. I couldn't tell if he'd seen me or not. I worried he'd think I had deliberately blanked him even though I had genuinely not seen him, and wondered again how on earth my radar hadn't picked him up, seeing as it so often detected him at long distances. It was as though some sort of self-protective mechanism was in force, preventing me from getting too close. This protective force was more powerful than I realised or gave it credit for. It was the Universe at work again, always wiser, always with long-range, panoramic vision, always working for the growth of our souls, not our egos.

It wasn't long before the actors took to the stage. It was a strange play, with some of the actors seeming to be somehow overcompensating, perhaps because the audience was so sparse. With Charlie, perhaps it was because he hadn't performed for a long stretch, not since the night at the Edinburgh Fringe, which was nearly six months ago. Charlie performed well, as he always did – but there was a peculiar tension and it wasn't a comfortable show to watch. Annie and I sat back around the middle of the theatre, but we had a perfect view as it was a small space. I watched the man who was standing in the middle of that stage, the man who'd been standing in the middle of my head, seeming to hold it captive, who'd been holding my heart, leaving me in such a muddled, aching mess since I'd placed that letter in his hands on the streets of Edinburgh.

I watched with an unusual degree of detachment.

It felt strange to hear his voice and see his physical form with my physical eyes again. Emotional though it was, I felt oddly disconnected, like I was bandaged up in cotton wool which was muffling the intensity. It may have been because I'd resorted to that sleeping tablet the night before and I was still mildly groggy. I had no intention of making a habit of slipping pills in my mouth but I'd felt that without some sleep I just couldn't get through this thing, and perhaps that slightly numbed feeling I had was because I was unaccustomed to opiates, but perhaps it was also because I was finally dealing with some of this stuff, and some healing had taken place, even if I still felt like a wreck.

After the performance, Annie and I got a drink and I sat back on a comfy chair and perked up a bit, feeling like I'd seen him, I was still in one piece and now he would likely disappear and I could get on with the rest of my life without him – or so I attempted to believe. We sat and chatted and I felt more relaxed until suddenly we realised Charlie hadn't disappeared as I'd expected him to. No, he was standing close to the bar with some of his friends. He had the air of a guy hanging around, waiting for something or someone, again trying to seem casual but appearing at least slightly on edge. I then realised he was looking my way and to my utter astonishment he seemed to have that look on his face, that look of old, that look of... love.

This is where two opposing feelings rose in me and began an inward battle there on the spot. One was relief. Relief that I could see he must still have some feelings or he would surely not look in 'that way' – but the other feeling was frustration. Frustration that, if he *did* have those feelings, why were we in this situation in the first place? He looked across the room at me and it seemed that nothing had properly changed, despite the chasms I felt I'd been crawling through. How could he stand there looking the same? Assuming he was still getting married – which was still the case from everything I'd heard – why was he gazing towards me with that soft, loving, longing look? I knew I *could* be mistaken, yet this whole thing had always run on deep instinct and people don't just stare that way for no reason – or at least I'd never met anyone who did. I could feel it, as though he was willing me to walk over, melt under his gaze and become the besotted, devoted girl I'd always been with him.

My new sense of self-preservation must have kicked in, because I didn't move. Not because I didn't care, not because I didn't love him, not because I was playing games. It was because it would have landed me back in a bigger mess than I was already in. It would have been a moment. A moment where we would have scintillating eye contact and those soulful transmissions would occur and... and then what? Then what? As Zharha had pointed out to me many times, those moments could be truly magical but unless they were backed up with decisive action on his part, they weren't doing me any good any more. If he wasn't prepared to make the changes needed to follow through, to let this love open up the way it was crying out to do, then it was back to walking away. I struggled with the pull but I didn't budge. It felt akin to trying to hold back a river that was demanding to rage forward, yet alongside that sensation was another invisible force, protecting me, barring me from making moves. He didn't linger too long and neither did Annie and I. It was time to get out of that place.

We walked forwards not long after Charlie had disappeared. Standing in a dark passage lined with various stage and screen posters I saw two exits – a main exit and a side exit. Without hesitation or analysis I went towards the side exit and soon we were out under the silent, starry, January sky.

I began walking with determination across a lumpy gravel car park as Annie revealed quietly, "Charlie's over there." I glanced behind and yes, there he was, standing at the other exit. The pull was present again but we kept walking and walking, crunching through the gravel. Once out of the car park we walked in a directionless manner for a bit. I felt all kinds of emotions welling up inside. I suddenly desperately wanted to see him, to speak to him. I felt heartless and out of character by doing this 'walking away' thing. Annie and I circled the block as a light frost began to build on the windscreens of parked cars. I remember seeing one of the other actors from the play, who I knew vaguely, staring at us from outside a pizza restaurant. After a few more minutes of walking I asked Annie meekly if we could go back, so I could just say hello to Charlie. Annie agreed, if it was what I wanted, but I felt she thought it was a mistake and it probably was. We headed back even though I knew deep down that he wouldn't still be there. I was right. He'd been whisked away, I expect by that same force that had held me back from crossing the room earlier. In hindsight, this was surely for the best.

Soon we were standing on the platform waiting for the Northern Line. By this point, I was fighting back tears. I was worried that I was just never going to get over this man. With all my good intentions I still had way too much energy invested in this. Nobody else had ever got to me like this. Breaking up is always hard to do and previous attachments from the past had all healed in the end, but with Charlie it was different and the strange thing, in a logical sense, was that we had never even been together in the traditional sense of a relationship. This surely wasn't normal. It *wasn't* normal. That was the point. This *was* something else and comparing it with traditional relationships was always a mistake. Yet, I had no other real frame of reference. If I'd listened to my soul instead of my chattering head it might have helped, but I couldn't shut my head up. I told myself that I was going to have to find a way out of this. There *must* be a way. I'd have to stay away next time, next performance, next time would be different. I wouldn't let it get to me.

There wasn't another performance for a very long time...

But there was another way. I wasn't quite there yet though, and had a lot of layers as well as tears to shed, and a lot of facing up to do. I wasn't the hopeless case I thought I was. I was just involved in a phenomenon that leaves no stone unturned, that demands a completely different way of understanding the Universe. I was right in the middle of the dark night of the soul so often described by the mystics of old, so often experienced before a major switching on of that brilliant cosmic light. The one that will never go out. On that cold January night that light was hard to discern, but that doesn't mean it wasn't there. And you know, it makes an awful lot of sense that in order to discover that cosmic light and to be guided by it, you come face to face with it through another human being, one that activates a light in your heart for them that will never go out. To identify that eternal flame in human form helped me to comprehend more fully that there is a higher power, a universal source of loving energy that will never go out either. Knowing that, trusting that, living with that in your heart is the only real answer I've found.

Thirty-Five

I came to believe that none of this was accidental, no matter how much it sometimes felt like something had gone horribly wrong with my life story and the Universe was cruel and random. There is a rhyme and a reason but until we stand back and view the bigger picture it's easy to think there isn't. For as long as the mind tries to work it out and explain it all away it will not make sense. It's all to do with listening to the soul rather than the ego. If that sounds simplistic, well, it is, in some ways, but since most of us have spent most of our lives doing the opposite it takes a lot of unlearning and remembering and there I was stumbling again and again, wanting to understand with my head something that was fundamentally energetic and spiritual. At the end of the day, I was a physical being as well as a spiritual being so a grand struggle was almost inevitable. What I didn't seem to get was that it was up to me when I stopped struggling. Only I could make that choice.

A few weeks after that performance, I ran into Jay one evening in Cafe Noir. To my shock he revealed he was upping sticks and moving away to his homeland in the Highlands. I wished him well but I was sad to see him go. It was like another significant piece of the backdrop of my life had been removed. A whitewashed canvas was being wheeled onto the stage, waiting to be daubed and splashed with new patterns. I knew it was better for Jay as he often spoke of missing the clean air, the mist and the mountains.

I saw nothing of Charlie for several months. It was as though the Universe was making sure we were kept apart, as plays and performances had been one of the main places we'd seen each other in recent times. The landscape remained bleak and bare, but I kept searching for answers, kept trying to keep my head up. I was still having a lot of trouble sleeping. I was still feeling a vague anxiety almost all the time.

I threw myself into various types of 'healing', hoping something would dull the pain, hit the magic spot that would release me from my torment. I enjoyed acupuncture and it did give me some relief. The lady who worked on me as I lay on a couch in her treatment rooms in Clapham was obviously intuitive. I presented myself as having trouble sleeping, fatigue and headaches, but after sticking a few needles in various points of my body and looking down at me with sweet compassion she said, "You've got a broken heart. Have you lost someone very dear to you?"

I told her I had but that I was getting 'over it' nicely. I never wanted to look weak and pathetic, or as if I was pining after some guy who didn't give a damn. Despite everything I still thought Charlie did care about me. But really, at this point, that was neither here nor there.

My acupuncturist helped ease the pain somewhat, and I felt bursts of my old self pop through here and there. I had six treatments and then decided I should be OK now, as though healing the soul could ever be given a scientific prescription, as if healing can ever be measured that way. I also started taking some nutritional supplements that Zharha recommended. I wasn't ill, but I wasn't well. What was wrong with me? Hadn't I been a perfectly normal, healthy young woman up to recent times? The truth of the matter was that what I'd been going through emotionally, mentally and spiritually had taken its toll physically. My adrenals were impaired through prolonged stress, fear, and the trauma of shattered dreams. The long-term strain was wearing me down. Along with this, as I was still developing my own abilities to help heal others, my vibrations were changing. Spiritual energy kept running through me, trying to unclog me, to wake me, to lift me up to higher frequencies. This was a good thing but the process can be physically disorientating as well as scary. Zharha encouraged me to surrender to the Universe. I came close and I could begin to give in for a while, but fear tended to grab me before I could really let myself fall. I was hanging halfway off that cliff for a long time, worried no one would catch me, worried I'd never find my way back, worried I'd lost Charlie forever, worried I was losing myself.

About three months after that last performance our paths crossed again. Thomas, one of the Last Exit Players who had now also joined another drama group, was having a birthday party, which I was invited to. Once again, I was a bag of nerves before the event, worried about encountering Charlie and the great unknown of how we would react to each other. It had been so long since I'd been face to face with him and I still had no clue what he'd truly made of my letter. I knew he was getting married in the summer, which was a few months away. I no longer wondered about whether he might not go through with it. I'd accepted it was happening. He seemed miles away from me these days and I had no real expectations of anything changing.

Annie and I set off to Hudson's Cave, where Thomas' party was in full swing. As we got close I got the same horrible jitters I'd got when attending Charlie's last performance. This nameless terror gripped me by the throat, and if you'd asked what exactly I was scared of I couldn't have articulated it. Why should seeing him throw me this much? I asked Annie if we could walk round the block as something was again steering me off our intended path. Thankfully Annie had no problem with a minor detour and understood my apprehension. We walked around the block, by which time I'd pulled myself together enough to walk on up to the door of the bar, ready to face the music.

No sooner had we reached the wide-open door than Danielle appeared in its frame. She looked furious to see us. I paused at the door, as did she, blocking the way through. I could tell that she was waiting for someone and I knew very well who that someone was. There he was. Face to face. Oh my God!

"Hello," we both said, both low-key, both somehow powerless. He was pale and uncomfortable and I guess I was the same. I went in with Annie and he went out with Danielle. OK, it had happened now. We'd laid eyes on each other and said hello. That was all we would say for the entire night.

I can't say I enjoyed the party, though I did my best to

keep my energy even and not focus on Charlie. Danielle was actually more of a problem than him as she seemed intent on following me round. If I moved, so did she. Wherever I settled she'd end up behind me, in front of me, at the side. As I often sensed, she was pretending to be having a good time but I knew her hollering was hollow. As a lot of actors and musicians were in the house, several people got up onstage and offered up impromptu performances. Charlie got up and did a comedy sketch with Thomas and Keith that belonged to a production that had been written by Charlie and Jay many years before. This sent most of the crowd on a giggling trip down memory lane. I watched the performance quietly with mild amusement, trying to breathe away my pain, all too aware of Danielle breathing down my neck.

After the performance I kept my distance from Charlie and Danielle as much as possible. He did look at me in an almost pleading, apologetic way at one point but we didn't speak. I left feeling much the same as I had before. I was becoming resigned to the facts. He was getting married and my love for him had to hide. It still felt horribly wrong but all I could do was keep trying to make my life right, to do what I felt was the right thing, and I tried. I tried so hard.

Thirty-Six

Summer arrived in South London and I was still struggling. Despite the beauty and vibrancy of that season my world felt drained of colour. For that stretch of time it seemed as though a lake of cold, grey water had flooded my world. It was always there, sometimes just lapping against my ankles so I could appear to function semi-normally, sometimes forcing me to wade waist-high through its groggy, groaning body. A certain greyness – if greyness can be certain – had descended and it scared me because I wasn't sure if it would ever leave; if this dismal, lapping, lacklustre lake would ever evaporate and allow me to walk on dry ground again. It scared me because this was no life. This wasn't living. This was surviving, and I knew very well this was not what anyone's life should be about. I was in an odd position of knowing that I was currently passing through something that felt almost inevitable and knowing I had to get through it. I had to pass this route but really wasn't sure if I could or how I could. I had to save myself. Whatever it took, I was now prepared to do it. I would find a way. I was determined to reclaim my happiness and purpose.

I managed to hold my job together but some days were hard and I spent them like a zombie. Sleeping poorly most nights, I'd sit on the bus wrapped in my drab coat of worries, wondering what the hell would become of me. My entire body ached and I simply got through my tasks like a robot with a band of tears positioned behind its eyes as June became July and the world kept on turning. Somehow I kept every appointment and deadline. I held a strange sort of self-discipline that kept me at least appearing to be vaguely normal, though I wondered about my office colleagues' unspoken thoughts. They couldn't miss the dark circles under my eyes, the dark circles around my soul, the lack of joy in my every move. Luckily I didn't stay in that place too long – but I stayed long enough to know I never wanted to go back there, and long enough to know that life *did* go on without Charlie. I came out the other side of it when I declared that taking care of myself was my priority. If that meant letting him go, then there it was. I let go slowly, though, so slowly and unsurely, but I knew it was the only road back to well-being.

I made a breakthrough when I realised that all my incessant doing and attempted fixing was actually part of the problem. I worked so hard on trying to solve my problems that I forgot what it was like to just let it be, to just sit with myself without beating myself up about being so sad and anxious, about not being able to do something as simple as fall asleep. My problems with sleeping were crucial in teaching me about the importance of letting go. I fought such a war with insomnia the year that Charlie got married. I made my bed a battlefield for a while by putting so much effort into trying to do something that you just can't force yourself do. You have to let it happen. You have to allow it to happen. Gradually, I learned to stop fighting all the battles I had created for myself, battles with not being able to fix everything and everyone, and not being able to let Charlie go. I couldn't force myself to stop loving him. I learned bit by bit to let it be. Slowly, I began to feel better about everything. I looked better, I slept better; I was coming out of my tunnel, inch by inch.

A day finally came when I could truly state that I loved life and it was sure worth living, with or without Charlie, without my life being perfect, noticing that imperfection has its own beauty. I'd reached a turning point. Sweet surrender became my mantra. There was nothing superficial about any of this, everything dug deep, right to my very bones (no wonder they seemed to ache so much) – but as I let the light in, everything literally got lighter. I kept on going and the murkiness started to recede and colour crept back in. The gut-wrenching pain gave way as I surrendered and found I no longer had to crawl, as I could see the light pouring through the exit of the tunnel and I could choose to keep crawling – or I could jump up and run towards it. Yes, it was real; it was there. I hadn't been forsaken.

I may have learned the hard way but I now knew that no person or prop was the answer. Society and the media work overtime to try and convince us that happiness comes from external constructs and conditions, whether they are material objects or objects of romantic affection. For as long as the 'pathway to happiness' hype is believed, many of us are trapped in a spiral of emptiness. The props had to completely collapse. I opened my fists, I uncurled my fingers and felt a gentle breeze tickling my palms. I let those props go and to my amazement, yes, I could stand up, all on my own. The breeze became a wind that could blow right through my soul and clear out all the crap that had huddled there for so long. The sun could embrace my shoulders and hug and nourish me. I hadn't been abandoned and I was stronger than I ever realised, because it wasn't all about me, it wasn't all about him – it was bigger than that. So, so big and beautiful! The Universe will have its way, and thank goodness for that.

I saw him one more time before he got married. It was probably about two weeks before his big day. My mother had come down from Manchester to stay and we were walking from the Tube station one Saturday around noon. As we got close to Cafe Noir I felt that old familiar pull and looking across the road I shouldn't have been surprised to see a familiar figure – two familiar figures. I saw Charlie and Danielle and a third person I didn't know occupying an outside table. It was like an instant knife in the chest for some reason. I had no idea why it crushed me to see him at that moment. Perhaps it was because there'd been some time apart and I was working hard on keeping the door closed. I didn't say a word to my mum as this was just too complicated to even begin to explain. Charlie appeared to be intently watching us when I first became aware he was there. As soon as he saw me clock him he seemed to visibly panic. I quickly looked away and carried on walking, noisily pulling along my mum's case on its scuffed wheels beside me on the uneven pavement. Why now? Why again? Why? Why? Why? Was the intensity ever going to fade?

Late autumn, something led me to look more deeply into the concept of soul connections, including what some refer to as twin souls and twin flames. I'm not sure what the impetus was. Maybe I hadn't been ready before. Maybe it's best to have lived through a healthy slice (or unhealthy slab) of this experience before viewing it through this particular lens. I did some research on the internet and even bought a couple of books. Most of what I read made sense to me, even though what was becomingly increasingly clear was that this whole thing wasn't about making sense. It bypassed logic and went straight to the heart and soul, which don't operate in logical manners and can't be understood intellectually. I read about signs and symptoms of meeting a person you shared a strong soul connection with and generally found I could tick all the boxes. There were lists of stages that these 'relationships' tended to go through, and yes, I could recognise those too – how it was common for one (or both) 'twins' to run away from the connection (mainly through fear), and how absolutely devastating that could be to both. How ultimately all you could do was surrender and recognise there was a bigger purpose at work and this *wasn't* a normal relationship, and any attempt to try and rationalise it or make it fit the everyday mould was futile. It was also very clear to me that ticking boxes and seeking external validation, though understandable, were only temporary assurances. This was all about going within and daring to trust yourself, which is easier said than done when you continue to allow your ego to play games with you.

Yet, the suggestion was that if both people did the work they needed to do on themselves, this could be something very special indeed. It *was* something special indeed already, as twin souls, if they do exist as described,

240

are very rare. I felt sure this is what I'd been dealing with all this time with (and without) Charlie. Perhaps now that he had chosen to get married, and in doing so erected a long-term roadblock to our being together, I was being guided to understand these energies more clearly and navigate my way forward. Much of what I read suggested happy endings, reunion after both parties had done the necessary 'work' on themselves. There were also suggestions that when you had learned your lessons and found your equilibrium you may choose *not* to be with this person, even if they are down on their knees and begging you, simply because you understand that the relationship isn't something you *need* any more and you know your happiness doesn't depend on it. This wasn't something I could easily imagine happening in my case with Charlie, but unimaginable things had already happened so I remained open-minded. I had already decided to do my work, although I was still semi-reluctant from time to time. There was this sense of dragging my heels through the dust instead of walking briskly along the path, though at least I believed I was on the path and some greater power seemed determined to keep me there.

What exactly was my path? I wasn't totally clear but I knew it didn't involve sitting around moping, or pining for a married man, soul connection or not. I also knew instinctively that doing my work meant doing it for my own sake and the sake of humanity and the planet, not in the hopes that by doing it he would reappear. Oh no, it just couldn't and wouldn't work like that because one of the biggest lessons of all – and I'm sure this applies to anybody experiencing one of these types of connections

– is the challenge of learning to love yourself fully, and only then will you understand that you have to do it for your soul's evolution, because if you love yourself, that's what you'll *want* to do. Yes, you can hope he'll do the same and if he does, you've got a really good chance of a wonderful life together, but the goal is a wonderful life, with or without him.

The twin soul theory was fascinating and when I discovered there was a named phenomenon, a plausible explanation for this experience, I had moments of relief and understanding. I could apply this new knowledge to the roller coaster ride I'd been on for such a long time. I read about other people's stories and recognised many elements of my own struggle in them. I read about the significance of the numerical sequence 11:11 and how it symbolised twin souls – the yin and yang polarity, the oneness, the great merge. I was stunned when I learned that that the number eleven, and particularly two elevens together, tended to appear in strange synchronicities throughout the twin soul experience. Strangely enough, I had first met Charlie on the eleventh evening of the eleventh month. I also gasped when I backtracked through my diaries to discover the night he'd gone down on his knees to me in Hudson's Cave had also been the eleventh evening of the eleventh month. I was gobsmacked and intrigued by the fact that these numbers had been popping up all over the place for me for some time. Yet, I also took it all with a pinch of salt and though the signs were screaming at me to take note, I knew that even though I believed that Charlie and I did share this unusual spiritual bond, this knowledge didn't provide me with an answer or conclusion. I had enough reason to believe I may have met my twin soul, if there truly was such a thing, and that was the reason this whole experience had been so compelling, so tragic, so elating, so transformative, so magnificent – and so everlasting.

The thing was, though, what was I going to *do* with this information? What was I supposed to do now? Why had I met him? Why had he gone? It was helpful to understand what I had been living through but now the challenge was not just to keep living, but to live to the full, to embrace the world in a new way, with new eyes, with the ego taking a back seat and the soul paving the way. Balham High Road would be walked again and again, just as I'd always done, but the inner scenery was changing. I stared in wonder at each face I saw, each pair of eyes that smiled or stared at me, each soul that was journeying here also. It was time to not just wake up but get up, get out there and live. I'd done too much hanging around.

Thirty-Seven

Out of the blue, in the new year I received an email from the director of a local film production company who was interested in turning the play I'd written a few years back for the Last Exit Players, *Une Lumière Particulière,* into a screenplay and ultimately to create a film. He wanted me to work on the screenplay with him. I was hugely excited about the prospect as for some reason I'd always envisioned the play working more fluidly as a film than as a stage production.

A few days later I had a fruitful meeting with some of the film company in their offices in Putney. After much discussion we agreed to work on the screenplay and they also asked if I'd like to be involved in the casting. I paused and my heart fluttered almost in the same breath as it sank before answering. How could I tell them there was only one person who should play the role of the chief male protagonist, but I knew he wouldn't agree to do it? Charlie had helped develop that character and made him his own on the stage.

"I'll... I'd love to be involved in the casting," I found myself saying.

"Do you have anyone in mind," Damian, the director, asked, "for the role of Anton or Gabrielle?"

The office printer jumped into action, seemingly

of its own accord, behind me and stopped again just as suddenly, making me jump.

"I'm sure I can think of several people." I smiled, feeling my heart thumping quietly.

For some reason, I wanted Charlie to give me his blessing with the film even if he wouldn't agree to be in it. I was scared and conflicted about contacting him but I didn't want our personal situation to influence the professional. Thomas and Jay had played parts in the stage version too and I sent word in case they wanted to audition. Both were immediately enthusiastic and supportive. Charlie was initially unresponsive, but eventually aired his views, which were a strange mixture of appreciation and disapproval that didn't seem to make much sense to me. To my surprise Charlie suggested a group meeting to discuss the possibility of the Last Exit Players' involvement.

One chilly evening around mid-January I arranged to meet Charlie and Thomas in The Devonshire, a traditional kind of pub in Balham. Sadly Jay wasn't present as he was now living back in the Highlands but he had sent me his best wishes and said he was up for being involved with the film if they wanted his input. The other two players were also away at the time. Thomas and I arrived first and we sat at a circular table waiting for Charlie to show up. I couldn't pretend I wasn't nervous, but at the same time I wasn't as apprehensive as the last few times we'd been in the same vicinity. I hadn't seen even a glimpse of Charlie for around six months. In fact, this would be the first time I'd seen him since he'd got married in the summer. We sat sipping our drinks and chatting until Charlie appeared.

He indicated he was going to the bar to get a drink and I continued chatting with Thomas as normally as possible. Charlie returned from the bar and proceeded to shake hands with us both, which seemed oddly formal to me but naturally I shook his hand and we all began to talk. We talked about general things and the screenplay and film, along with the possibility of me recommending them for casting. After listening to my nervous spiel about the project, Charlie politely declined and I accepted that as fine. It was as I had expected, deep down.

How strange it felt to all be sitting together again after so long. At times, Charlie felt like a different person. He looked like Charlie, he spoke like Charlie but something was missing. The light in his eyes was subdued and he somehow gave the impression he'd been in hibernation for a while and was just coming out and smelling the air for the first time in months. He even commented on how different the decor in the pub appeared, which Thomas and I knew had been this way for some considerable time, and Thomas, puzzled, pointed this out. I couldn't quite put my finger on it but something was generally odd about Charlie. To be fair, he probably felt very uncomfortable too. He wasn't cold with me and made the occasional joke but I was aware he was being very careful and not wanting to engage too much. That was OK because I was on guard myself. I knew I still loved him but I was growing used to the fact that things were now different, no matter how much I wished it were otherwise. He'd made them different and I'd made them different as a result.

We all carried on talking in a relatively normal manner but the elephant that had stumbled into the bar with us was lounging ostentatiously on the sofa, impossible to ignore. I wondered what Charlie and I would have talked about if Thomas wasn't present, but it probably was for the best that he was. It made it impossible for references to my letter and its repercussions to enter the conversation. Again, this was probably for the best as what was there to say? If Charlie had wanted to respond to that letter, surely he would have done long ago. It was over a year since I'd given it to him and the only response had been silence. Silence speaks volumes, of course, but who can interpret those volumes? I'd decided to let the silence speak for itself. I wasn't sure if we'd ever be as close as we once were, or if indeed we would ever even see each other after this. It was a bittersweet experience to be so near him, yet feel so far away. We talked for the best part of an hour and then it seemed we all felt it was time to go.

I didn't mean to stare and quickly averted my eyes as he rose and hitched his jeans up. It may or may not have been deliberate, but he stood up and paused with his midriff right in my face, so that I couldn't help but be aware of his anatomy below the waist, even if he was fully clothed. Or was it just so long since I'd been in his presence that I was staring almost in disbelief that this was really him, in the flesh, at last? What struck me was the strange detachment I either naturally felt or had forced myself to feel. I'm truly not sure which. Since the engagement and subsequent marriage I'd marked him as physically out of bounds. Not that I would have ever intended to sleep with him when he was still with Danielle even before the engagement, but we had frequently touched each other playfully and affectionately as well as both planting the odd kiss without this ever feeling remotely wrong. The seriousness of marriage had provoked a withdrawal from me on many levels. Perhaps the most obvious withdrawal had been in the realm of physical desire. For my part it had always been there, even though it had never been allowed to creep much above the surface. Maybe it was a blessing in disguise that we had never done what might have been expected here. Perhaps it would have been even harder to let go. God knows it was hard enough.

Of course I still found Charlie physically attractive and know I always will, but the fact that he was now married took the sheen off things. I know for some people the forbidden is even more desirable but for me it actually had the opposite effect. I couldn't comfortably swallow illicit kisses no matter who they came from, and felt I had to try to block that sexual magnetism he seemed to emit so easily, like smoke curling in the air from a cigarette. I knew how I felt about him went way beyond our hormones, our physical features or biological programming and it always had done, but having said that, we were both human and I knew I had to try and shield myself from the impulse to even think about falling into bed with him. I felt a pang of pain as he zipped up his jacket and faced the door of the pub. I got to my feet and it felt a little awkward as we collectively moved towards the exit. Things never used to feel like this. Hanging with these guys had always been both comfortable and fun. Thomas talked to Charlie about meeting up or coming round and keeping more in touch. I wished I could do the same but knew I couldn't. I waited politely to excuse myself and slip away into the dark January night.

Charlie mentioned popping into Hudson's Cave to say hello to Hudson, addressing this more to Thomas than to me – not that he was excluding me because I knew he wasn't. Thomas opted to go with him and though part of me wanted to join them, to spend any moment I could with Charlie before the inevitable parting, I knew I had to resist that urge now. Now that things were different it was not very dignified to go bouncing around with him, as I would probably have done before. I said my goodbyes and forced myself to walk – one boot in front of the other – away. I had to get away from the one person I wanted so much to be with, to make that physical separation so I could once again face this pain and accept that things had changed and there was nothing left for me here. Thomas shouted goodbye and that he'd see me soon as I walked away, which caused me to look back and see the pair of them stood waiting for traffic to pass in the middle of Balham High Road. I saw Charlie wave uncertainly. Everything was now uncertain. It hurt. Everything hurt. I walked home and yes, I cried. Again.

The next day I received an early morning text from Thomas asking me how I was and saying he didn't know what Charlie's problem was or how he could not want to be involved in the film. I think he'd picked up my pain and the strangeness between Charlie and me, but I had no idea how little or how much he knew of our currently strained relationship. It was nice that he cared and thoughtful of him to check on me but I resisted the urge to tell him all about it. No, this was between me and Charlie and whatever *was* between us. Whatever this thing was, it was still there, a little muted perhaps, a little muddied, a little out of sync, left out in the rain but there was no denying – at least for me – that it was still there. So, maybe it always would be… but if that was the case, I didn't want this to be a prison sentence. I wanted to water and weed that thing between us, make it shine again, make it beautiful like it was supposed to be, regardless of whether we ever even spoke again. There was something precious and sacred between our souls and I couldn't toss it away no matter how much that's what most would probably advise. If I had to put it away, I would put it away, with care, with love, with peace. It was just figuring out how to do that. I'd make a positive out of this whole experience somehow. Maybe there was just still too much pain to shed first – more inner junk that these tears would erode – and sooner or later, when it was all cleared out, the sun would be visible, the path would be clear and I'd skip instead of walk.

Thirty-Eight

Work carried on with the film and Thomas and Jay became part of the production. Thomas played the role he had played in the stage version and Jay collaborated with the company's film crew in various ways involving scenery, costumes and lighting. Creatively I was thrilled about the project, yet the feeling was bittersweet due to Charlie's non-involvement. It felt strange converting the lines he'd said onstage into a screenplay without him looking over my shoulder, and I felt he had a strong contribution to make here, yet if he wasn't willing to make it, what could I do? It made little sense that he would shun a project like this, as it would certainly benefit his career. Yet, sadly and inexplicably, his stage career appeared to have completely stalled and the last that I heard was that he was working for a business owned by Danielle's father instead.

I guessed it would be far too awkward for him to work with me and pretend to be casual about everything. Perhaps I just peered into his soul too deeply and that made him uncomfortable. I didn't really set out to do this. I never attempted to use that X-ray vision that seemed to have been there most of the time since we'd met. It was automatic, instant, and information came both clairvoyantly and clairaudiently. There were feelings and impressions – his, mine, ours – that could just as easily have come from centuries ago as from yesterday. They just lunged into my space and I couldn't censor them even if I tried. You can't censor the soul, though I guess you can try to ignore it. I felt his energy swirling around me as I wrote the screenplay. He might as well have been sitting across the table from me at times. I worried about his rejection of my work, which he had always approved of before. Whatever I felt drawn to express in my writing was always pure, honest and written with love.

The letter I'd given Charlie in Edinburgh was written in the same spirit, but it was maybe too honest, too real, just too much to have spelt out in black and white on paper. Did I need to be more careful with what flowed from my pen? I wasn't sure because in my mind I was always respectful and sensitive, but the thing was – and I knew it and maybe he did too – that even if that ink was invisible, what floated between us and around us could be felt regardless of whether it was spoken or typed out in twelve-point Arial font. The energy was intense and it spoke out loud even if our lips were sealed.

One blustery but bright March day I was sent to a creative networking conference in Reading on behalf of *South of the River*. I was sitting on a panel for some of the day answering questions about my role with the magazine and the current state of the performing arts scene in South London. It was a busy and buzzy day and much as I enjoyed it I was exhausted by the time the agenda sheet was worked through and I could escape. I had a box load of promotional material from the magazine left over that I knew they wanted back, so I left for Reading train station weighed down and windswept. I thought about how well things were going for me since moving to London in terms of career, and felt mildly pleased with myself for what I'd achieved.

For the entire day I hadn't thought about Charlie. It wasn't often that this was the case, even if it was just a brief reminder or flashback. Sitting on the train, I shut my eyes for some of the journey, the box of leaflets on the seat beside me as the train charged madly through the largely industrial landscape. As we edged into Staines a subtle but familiar feeling crept over me and I felt my eyes surveying the people standing awaiting the train on the crowded platform. The carriages slowed down gradually before reaching a halt, and just as the halt happened my heart jumped when I saw Charlie was among the crowd of passengers waiting to board the train. *Oh my God!* I exclaimed inwardly as I saw he had a choice of the two nearest doors – one into my carriage and one into the carriage in front of me. With a mixture of excitement and panic I saw he chose the carriage I was in, though I supposed he couldn't have seen me when he made that choice. However, as he got on I felt sure he did see me, even though I dropped my head and tried to blend invisibly into the interior of the carriage. He chose a seat around two seats ahead of mine and sat down.

I was a nervous wreck for the rest of the journey, for no reason I can fully explain. For months I'd wanted to see him, yet now that he was riding on the same train, breathing the same stuffy air as me, why did his presence throw up so much fear? It was the million-dollar question in all this. How can a love so strong create so much fear? Fear of what? How come I didn't jump up and go sit beside him? I felt scared, overwhelmed and even though I knew it wasn't a rational fear it was very real. I kept my head buried in a book I had with me and prayed he hadn't seen me. If I could have made myself disappear in a puff of smoke, removed myself as quickly as I could, I would have done so.

Somehow I had a sense he was trying to draw attention to himself. He even stood up a couple of times for no reason other than appearing to adjust his coat. His phone rang and I heard him say, "Hello" and take a brief call in which he didn't seem to speak other than the initial greeting. Was that really his voice that had just spoken? Was that really him? Did he make this journey regularly? I felt strangely disinclined to speak to him, though I felt he wanted me to acknowledge him. Had he approached me, that would have changed things, but I didn't want to open anything up after all the hurt and pain of the last eighteen months. He'd made his position clear by his silence since my letter and his non-involvement with the film, so why would he even *want* to speak to me, I asked myself?

Yet, I was sure he did. That same old feeling. I didn't budge, and the feeling didn't budge either. I was terrified, and also my ego was worried I looked a bit of a state. My make-up wasn't fresh and I was having a bad hair day. Yet, though I used those superficial issues as excuses, they weren't the reason I was hanging back and of course I knew it. The energy was so strong and even seeing him in the first place, out of context, combined with the strange synchronicity of my carriage pulling up right at his feet, was so unbelievable it had sent me into some kind of stupid funk.

By time we got to Clapham Junction where I was due to get off, I was ready to run. I got up and edged my way to the door furthest from Charlie at the back of the carriage. He also got up and moved to the door nearest him. I was poised by the door with my eyes to the floor, scared to glance his way in case he made eye contact. As soon as the doors opened I bolted off the train like a terrified animal and ran up the steps to the bridge between the platforms like my life depended on it. I didn't look back and found myself on the wrong platform for Balham. I checked the display information on a screen and walked sheepishly back to the right platform, slowly beginning to get myself together again and feeling a fool. Within minutes I felt regret for running and acting like an idiot. My heart rate returned to normal and I marvelled at the strange encounter and my strange reaction. I remembered the reading I'd done on soul connections and how one of the pair, usually the man, though certainly not always, runs away, metaphorically or literally, freaked out by the intensity of feelings and energies evoked. The shoe was on the other foot today. I had the running shoes on and I'd sprinted faster than I ever knew I could whilst clumsily holding a heavy box of leaflets.

Later on, it occurred to me that perhaps this was how Charlie felt some of the time too. He'd run from me in numerous ways. Perhaps he'd even dived into another relationship in attempt to keep the fear away, to keep the scary feelings at bay, to try and normalise things. I wondered if that worked, and suspected it didn't. I told myself that if that fear gripped me ever again I'd overcome it. How on earth could we ever be together with that crazy running thing in the mix? But I also knew that sometimes when we had been together, fear could disappear out the window and over the hills. A beautiful peace would encircle us and when we both felt safe and surrendered, that energy became something else entirely. What I was learning was that something very powerful was demanding that those fears be overcome. Fear itself had to be dismantled and seen for what it is: something that usually falls apart when challenged and looked straight in the eye. I knew I had to choose love over fear… every time.

Every single time.

Thirty – Nine

So, Charlie and Danielle had been married for over a year now. The world kept on turning and the sun continued to rise and set and rise again over the red bus-filled South London streets I witnessed and walked through each day. Although it had taken a while I felt reasonably confident I had come through my dark night of the soul. Although I worried at times that I might relapse, my progress seemed steady and if I did have a bad day – which I did occasionally – it was much easier to get back on track. A lot of healing had happened and it all stemmed from a sense of acceptance and surrender and learning to love myself. And not just love myself but *be* myself, be *with* myself. It might sound strange but it's shocking how much time I spent disconnected from myself, trying to avoid myself, trying to dodge mirrors, looking outside myself for things that could only be found inside.

It didn't happen overnight but gradually I seemed to be emerging from my cocoon. I realised that time hadn't weakened my love for Charlie. I realised that I still loved him. I realised that loving him was the most natural thing in the world for me and that attempting to force myself to stop, to cut that precious bond, was not just futile but deeply distressing for my soul. A balance could exist here. I could learn to let the love be instead of trying to quell it, and as long as I loved myself just as much as him, there would be no pain any more. This was a new way of being. This was a new way of loving that wasn't driven by need, ego or inherited dysfunctional patterns of the past. Suddenly everything could be new again and I could let the past go – once and for all – and let the future be whatever it would be.

Zharha had suggested to me that I invite Charlie to talk to me in dreamtime. She said that there was a channel there that could be helpful to the healing process. In the past she'd built that dream shield to stop the torment. She no longer saw it as necessary, which pleased me. I knew the channel was always there and there'd been times when even the dream shield wasn't strong enough to hold back the energy if our souls felt an urgent need to communicate. Although I knew and had enough past experience to validate some of the stuff that happened in dreamtime, there had also been times when I'd tried to dismiss the messages and odd synchronicities that came through during the small hours of the morning. However, at this point I was less dismissive. I was daring to believe that there was a higher meaning to all of this, that there was so much more to life than the three-dimensional world we focus so much attention on. Why not use our night-line?

I began to view my unusual connection with Charlie in a positive light rather than something that had somehow trapped me in limbo, something that prompted growth and wisdom rather than a misfortune that had torn me apart. And it *had* torn me apart, but only so I could come out the other side so much stronger. I could learn the lessons that were crying out to be learned, and perhaps only something as earth-shatteringly powerful as the way Charlie had fallen into – and out of – my life was big and relentless enough to make sure I *did* learn. And I did. I was finally able to recognise how many of our external behaviours and impressions are just defence mechanisms, fear-induced reactions and ego-based assumptions. Once I did this it was all too easy to see and feel the love. The love had always been there and would always be there. Love wasn't something to be possessed or controlled, not something to be stored and hidden away. It was something that needed to flow, to expand, to light up the world, to just be, with no expectations or attachments. Joy rushed back to me when I saw it this way and let the stubborn doubts go.

Of course the doubts returned at times but I was able to catch them at the entrance to my heart, before they gatecrashed and jeered at the gentle peace that really was there all the time. Another big realisation I had was that this stuff was also wrapped up with other relationships in my life and many of them seemed to be changing also, either deepening and becoming more authentic or fading away. I noticed I didn't seem to have as many friends as I used to have, yet those I did have were more soulful and beautiful, emanating from a place of love and equilibrium rather than driven by habit or hunger. As a result I was rarely lonely. There was something about this whole experience with and without Charlie that had changed my understanding of love. I found myself feeling spontaneous outpourings of love for strangers, for people I saw from the top deck of the bus, huddling in bus shelters. I looked at their faces, at the imprints of time and emotion on their skin. I felt the same wave of tenderness for animals. I'd always loved animals but I felt a new connection, a connection with all creatures. How could one connection with one man be so powerful as to unlock my heart in this way?

I wasn't sure exactly what had happened but I knew that it was something to do with understanding that we all are truly connected. I'd always suspected it. I'd stare at the stars as a child, sitting on my bedroom windowsill in my pyjamas, wondering if anyone up there could see us in our little houses. I always sensed there were intricate, swirling lines of communication between all living things, seen and unseen. I'd always hoped that was the case. Now as an adult, instead of being dismissive of such thoughts, I was more sure that this is an orchestrated Universe, and we are all made of the same stuff. With that realisation came both a great joy and a great responsibility, to ourselves and each other. When I knew I could love Charlie, yet not have him in my life (even though I still wished he was there), I knew I could truly love, and somehow that meant I could truly live too. There was a new passion along with the new compassion. How exciting to be part of this web of wisdom and wonder. How exciting that my childhood sense of magic was allowed back into my life, and the rigidity that had attempted to replace it was in meltdown. Only I could give myself permission to be free. It was up to me.

The dreams never felt like 'just dreams' – they had an aliveness that never departed easily on waking. I wrote many of them down as they felt important – not just something to throw away and not pay attention to. I remember one which also featured Danielle around this time. In my dream I was positioned on a high platform and was watching her and Charlie on holiday in a hot country by a pool. She was lying down soaking up the sun on a towel with shades on, completely ignoring him as he slumped unhappily in a deckchair.

I could feel how bored and sad he was (even though I wasn't actually there, I was some way away watching the scene on a screen), so I called, "Hey, Charlie, why not break the monotony? Fancy a coffee?"

I thought he would ignore me, either because he wouldn't be able to hear at that distance or he wouldn't dare reply with Danielle nearby, but he got on his feet immediately and said, "I'm gonna get into trouble for this, but what the hell?" Then somehow he leapt across the big expanse of space to where I was on the high mountain platform, broke through the screen (which turned out to be made of paper) and stood beside me, grinning from ear to ear. I could hear his thoughts as sometimes I felt I had in real life: *I did it! I can do it!*

I woke up in my bed in Balham and sat up excitedly. *He can do it!*

The dreams kept on coming. Some were crystal clear; others were foggy and elusive. Charlie inhabited them frequently. He seemed to be trying to tell me something. The easiest way to describe the accumulated messages was that he was working on his stuff and yes, he did love me, and that maybe, one day…

Yet, it wasn't all 'maybe, one day' in many of the dreams. In some we were clearly together and all our

261

ridiculous daytime real-world fears and ego needs fell away like a house of cards. In another place, we could see each other for what we truly were without all our dysfunctions. I began to wonder which was real, and my uncertain conclusion was that perhaps they both were, it was just a matter of perspective.

It felt to me that many of the dreams were about us coming to terms with things and healing, but I also felt there was more to it that I couldn't quite understand, as though it could be having some positive impact on him and just *maybe*, it might help him find a way out of the conundrum he seemed stuck with. Not necessarily to me, but to a place that was happier for him. I never stopped hoping that for him, and I also hoped we could properly be friends on the earthly plane again, regardless of romance.

I bumped into Charlie for the first time in ages – the first time since on the Reading train a couple of months back. Annie and I had popped into a supermarket in Colliers Wood one Sunday afternoon to get some provisions. The moment I walked in the door I felt a sensation like a very gentle breeze that seemed to be asking me to pay attention. I looked in the distance and saw a woman in a beige raincoat marching along the frozen fish aisle. She immediately reminded me of Danielle. I largely dismissed it but mentioned it to Annie as we carried on selecting fruit and vegetables.

"Er, think I *might* have seen Danielle," I reported apprehensively, continuing to feel my senses heightening the way they tended to do when Charlie was in the house. It didn't take long for me to realise the marching woman was indeed Danielle, accompanied by Charlie, who was pushing their trolley slowly around the store.

We came face to face at the bottom of an aisle and I made sure I stood my ground and looked him right in the eyes, even though the insane urge to run had hit me. Somehow, though, I managed to fight off the fear, which just wanted to scoop me up, like a panic-stricken arm trying to yank me back to the fruit and vegetables, but no, I was standing my ground and so was he.

"Hello, how are you?" I asked him, four simple words. He said similar short words back but the energy was what mattered, not what we said.

Danielle stomped off as soon as Charlie opened his mouth to greet me. He smiled a lot and his body language became animated and excited, almost like it used to before things got so complicated. It was a brief encounter but it was an important one for me because it told me we could get past the hurt of the past, we could relight this fire. In fact, it was already burning and had never gone out. When I moved on down another aisle I saw them again at a distance and sadly I saw that Danielle appeared to be reprimanding him... again. Oh, and the weirdest thing was that he was wearing a checked blue-and-white shirt exactly like he'd worn in that dream where he punched through the paper screen to reach where I was, saying, "I did it! I can do it!"

Previously I had asked the angels/guides (whoever those powerful beings that talked to me were) if they could give me some sign that these dreams meant something. This had been just before Annie and I had left to go for a walk before driving back via Colliers Wood, so within

263

hours of my request, this supermarket encounter had occurred. I felt I could really trust it now and that it was all for good, whatever it all really meant. What pleased me greatly was that I felt no upset or attachment upon seeing him – nothing but a pleasant buzz. And even Danielle's angry energy didn't throw me. I was just really pleased that neither of us had given in to the fear. We were beginning to be able to behave normally instead of one or other of us running away. We were choosing love, not fear.

I retold many of my dreams to Zharha and to Annie, both of whom listened patiently to my nocturnal diaries. I hoped I didn't bore them but sometimes these dreams were so epic, so tinglingly real I felt I had to relay them to somebody. There were many remarkable ones, especially around this time, that felt extraordinary, and on and off the voices I had begun to call my guides seemed to emerge within this realm, perhaps finding it easier to get through to me in receptive sleep mode. One of those dreams in particular left me with the most beautiful afterglow that barely faded for the whole of the next day. I can even feel it now if I close my eyes.

I'd gone to bed early, just before ten, because I was feeling I needed to sleep. Lying in my bed, before I fell asleep I had the strangest feeling – an excitement; I felt like a child going to bed on Christmas Eve, like something hugely exciting and important was about to happen. I was aware of the feeling as something external, as though it was hanging in the air outside the window like a mist – so strange and like nothing I can quite compare it to. I thought it was odd because there was no conscious cause and Charlie was actually not on my mind at all. Despite the excited feeling I fell asleep quickly and slept soundly until about 4am, then awoke.

I lay there in a relaxed mode, thinking of nothing in particular but still being aware of the magical feeling glistening softly outside the window. After around thirty minutes I fell asleep again until my alarm woke me and plucked me out of this 'dream'. It was more than a dream, with many chapters and characters, but the part I recall most vividly involved me sitting on a long sofa with Charlie on one side and Annie on other. Danielle sat on other side beside Charlie. We were watching some kind of romantic black-and-white film in an amazing top-storey apartment with magnificent stained glass windows that looked out across the city. Charlie kept edging closer to me and I did the same. We were talking delightedly, so happy to be together, and kept leaning over to each other to speak and laugh. Even though I was enjoying our cosy playfulness, I was aware that Danielle would likely be cross. Although I was worried about what she might do, somehow we just didn't seem to be able to stop, even if we wanted to. We kept touching each other's arms and shoulders. He was so in tune with me and I with him.

Our touching soon turned into kissing, at which point Danielle finally reacted and said, "What the hell do you think you're doing?"

I paused and waited for the inevitable argument, but instead Charlie politely said to her, "I have to take care of my baby" (meaning me), and he took me to another room.

Once alone together at last, there was no holding back and we were soon lying on a shimmery bed in front of the windows that framed the stars and London skyline. We had sex and it felt like the first time and the thousandth time. I was struck by his incredible blend of gentleness and passion. I felt so utterly wrapped in love, so safe, so right, so good, that I was simply speechless.

Then he said to me, "I don't want you to ever doubt I love you – ever."

Incredulous that anything could feel this intense and wonderful, at one point I said, not exactly to him but to the room, "Is this *really* Charlie doing this?"

The response, as he continued to make love to me in that gentle, exquisite way, was a sea of heads (misty spirit heads) nodding. *Yessss.*

All through the next day I kept that feeling of being wrapped in his love. A certain kind of light lit every space I stepped into. I'd felt his arms around me in many dreams before, and there'd be sexual scenes on and off in our astral meetings, but this one stood out. I remembered the words he said – "Don't ever doubt!" – and it was such a strong and clear instruction that I had to believe him. I would have trusted him with my life. I believed in him and I believed in the dream. On some level it was completely real, as real as anything I've ever lived through.

Forty

There would be backsliding days – backsliding phases where thoughts of him and the acute longing for him and for resolution seemed to invade my being mercilessly – but these became fewer and shorter in duration. When I surrendered and handed it over to the Universe I experienced an almost immediate end to the angst. So, why couldn't I remain permanently in surrender mode? That is a good question but expectations, memories, happenings and triggers will always lurk and sometimes catch you when you least expect it. It was also a question of keeping disciplined – meditating regularly, eating reasonably healthily, taking time to care for my body and soul. Still, he was never truly far from my thoughts.

I was always looking for him. Often this was just a subconscious impulse. I'd step outside, I'd be in a crowded room, I'd be at an airport or train station and on some almost involuntary level my antennae were switched on, hoping to intercept his signal, hoping for a chance encounter. Maybe this was partly because we'd had so many chance encounters, so often accompanied by a fateful feeling. Maybe it was just because my soul yearned for him, night and day. I'd scour the landscape, hoping to catch a glimpse of his tousled head, his familiar outline, his cheeky grin, even though that grin was rarely visible these days. Some part of me was still wishing that he'd step out of the ether and greet me the way he often had in the past.

I'd walk past all our familiar haunts, Hudson's Cave, Cafe Noir, Ceiling or even the local takeaways, and glance searchingly through the panes of glass, looking for his scent, looking for his eyes, looking for his simple presence. And if I found it, or even glimpsed it, my entire being would light up like a Christmas tree. These days, he didn't seem to be in the places we used to go. He didn't seem to be anywhere I went. I'd cast my eyes across each South London landscape I inhabited but all I saw were lonely skies, magpies, muddy puddles and people wrapped in big coats with little dreams. *Where are you, Charlie?* my soul would whisper. *Where are you? Where are you?*

Yet, maybe one of the things I needed to learn was that physical presence isn't the only kind of presence. How come I could close my eyes and it was as if he was there beside me? How come when I was miles away – maybe visiting my family back up north – he'd show up in a dream, thought or feeling, puncturing the distance with an energy so strong it was as if he'd just stepped off the train at Piccadilly and come to see me? And of course this wasn't only possible with Charlie, though it was more pronounced. Most of us have experienced the phone ringing and known it is the person we've just been thinking about. But what does it all mean? I still struggled with understanding the difference between the physical and metaphysical worlds. It seemed to be something that Charlie had come into and out of my life to show me.

October came round, wrapping the pavements in a glorious leaf blanket. So too did an opportunity finally come round for me to see Charlie again. As part of my role with *South of the River* I'd organised a mini festival at Hudson's Cave to celebrate the work of new playwrights with some Arts Council funding that had unexpectedly come our way. Somehow, without any deliberate engineering from me, it happened that Charlie would be involved with one of the performances, which was quite a surprise for me as he'd not been working in theatre at all for some time. Although I was nervous about seeing him and how the land lay between us I was still feeling ultimately positive, not expecting anything in particular but open to whatever the situation offered. Much more peace was in the mix for me now as I'd already said goodbye to the majority of the angst of yesteryear.

Still, old habits die hard and I felt a little worried as I left the flat and walked the half-mile to Hudson's Cave. Old habits die hard but oh, they can die; they can fade away; they can be overcome and here I was standing outside the door of the Cave, realising the man of my dreams was inside, seemingly on his own, or so it appeared when I peered through the window. I could see him fiddling around with the sound system through the glass panes. It was mildly dizzying just to know he was inside that door, and I could hear music loud and clear as I stood at the door. He was playing an old track by a local band called the Shore, who we both rated and had discussed in the past. It was called *Dialling Your Number* – a song that I could easily relate to, especially within the context of the life I'd recently lived through, the acres of yearning and doubt that had almost engulfed me, as that was kind of the subject of the song. Strangely enough, or perhaps not strangely at all, I'd heard this particular song playing like a record in my head as I'd walked along Balham High Road moments earlier. I knocked on the door, unsure if Charlie could hear me or see me. Even though part of me was scared I stood my ground, took a deep breath and faced the beautiful music.

As *Dialling Your Number* came to an end there was silence other than the muffled sound of his footsteps as he came down to the door and let me in.

"Thanks," I said, stepping inside, and we made some small talk before he went back to the mixing desk and put on something else. I don't know where Hudson or the other actors were but nobody appeared for some time. Within minutes of the next record coming on and Charlie standing there looking at me smilingly I knew everything was alright, but I scarcely dared believe it. As the night went on it felt as if we'd both made a decision to face each other honestly and lovingly. It seemed as though we'd both gotten over 'it' – whatever 'it' was. This thing that caused so much pain was largely ego and conventional expectation, living in the head instead of the heart, letting the blue funk lead the way, instead of letting love *show* the way. This love was never meant to have a lid put on it. It was meant to be allowed to breathe, to flow and nourish both of us as well as others. It was there, in that room, as palpable as the sawdust on the floor. In some ways it felt like a time warp; in some ways it was nothing to do with the past, it was new, it was different even though on the surface it was similar to scenes we'd both lived through before – but now we had the benefit of new wisdom, old love made new, love that just refused to die.

And here's the rub – it was also a love that refused to be defined. That natural tendency to box it up as romance wasn't entirely gone – in fact it wasn't really gone at all, but the understanding that this was beyond categorisation was liberating. In its truest essence love is just love, and demands nothing. The love I felt for Charlie refused to be typecast no matter how many times I tended to view it through that heart-shaped window. It didn't mean we couldn't have romance – not at all – it just meant it wasn't capable of being contained in any rigid sense. It existed as pure one hundred per cent love, needing nothing but to be, to flow, to warm the world and simply shine! I'd never use the expression 'just friends' again. There was nothing limiting about what existed between us unless we tried to slap a definition on it.

What could be more than this? We could be everything we already were... We still had some distance to go but that night showed me clearly that this wasn't all in my head. This bond between us, though highly unusual, was absolutely real. And it wasn't all over. It was alive and well but the path from here was not one I could currently see, guess or know. It was all about walking the path, not seeing where it ended. It was as though beautiful willow trees bent low to kiss that path, adding to its enchantment by keeping everything but one step ahead hidden – hidden until you walk along it and gently push those branches back. All I knew was that I had to keep walking – and I did.

An hour or so later, I was checking tickets as the

audience rolled up at the Cave. Charlie wasn't due onstage until a little later and instead of hanging out in the dressing rooms he stayed at a table close to me at the door. I could feel his eyes on me much of the time and it was that same old feeling, except, as I said, it was brand new too. I'd come out the other side of the tunnel, more or less, and I sensed he'd had his own tunnel to struggle through. I didn't know if he had emerged from it or was still searching for the light at the end, but though our trials may have been different I got the impression they were somehow intrinsically linked, and without knowing the details I sensed he'd been to hell and back, as I had myself. But for tonight, I had a little piece of heaven. I have to admit that just being near each other again was pure bliss, and especially as he seemed to be saying all the right things. It felt too good to be true, yet I did believe my eyes – and ears.

Charlie said some things that night that surprised me. What they demonstrated was that he too was working on facing fear… just like I'd been. He admitted to me he'd nearly chickened out of performing but had forced himself to go through with it. Annie turned up an hour or so after the doors opened and I could see some apprehension in her eyes as she came up to me, telling me she'd just seen Charlie outside having a cigarette and how were things? Poor Annie. She'd lived through so much of this too and I'll be eternally grateful to her for always being so supportive. Tonight, for a change, I could give her good news.

"Things are fine." I beamed, barely believing what I was saying. Charlie came back inside, smiling too, and it didn't take long for Annie to see that it was true. Things were fine. Things would always be fine if we just allowed them to be.

It felt so natural to talk to Charlie again, and I remembered that's how it had always been. Even the arrival of Danielle a little later or Hudson barking on about ticket sales didn't bother me. I didn't see much of Danielle that evening but I do remember her standing guard over Charlie at a couple of points, but somehow the chains didn't seem as heavy that night. She also frogmarched him out of the Cave when it was time to go as I'd often seen her do before, but again, he seemed to be walking with more abandon than had been the case in recent times, and though I couldn't quite say he had a spring in his step, he wasn't dragging his heels either. He said goodbye to me politely and his eyes flashed me a message of big but semi-muted emotion, which I received like a telepathic bundle of muddled hopes and fears, as well as love. Danielle marched by, ignoring Annie and me as loudly as she could. It didn't bother me anything like it used to. I'd come too far and there was no going back to moping or pining. I loved him every bit as much as I ever did but I had a much better sense of self now, a much better balance and understanding of what this was all about.

A few days after Charlie's performance, I was back in Hudson's Cave. This time it was to catch a young local band because a journalist friend of mine had recently featured them in her magazine and thought they'd be up my street. Stepping inside the door, I could almost catch a

273

sweet, lingering scent of my recent encounter with Charlie. The joint was jumping and I was feeling upbeat. Even though there were hundreds of unanswered questions in the air, my mood was mellow since seeing him. Somehow, these days I let those questions go a lot more easily. Things were getting better. I trusted my instinct on that but at the same time I wasn't exactly looking for a particular response from Charlie because I knew that it was futile to wait for him to make changes that suited me, even though that tendency hadn't been entirely eradicated. It was something I wanted to eradicate and I was working on it. I was happy that some warmth had been re-established between us because it sure felt like that was how it was supposed to be, but I tried to resist wanting to make it any more than that. My job was to focus on my own development and healing and the realisation that Charlie or no Charlie, I was finally OK. Yes, I was, and that was a mild shock in itself.

My friend arrived and we chatted to some of the band and admired their home-grown merchandise laid out on a table inside the door. I picked up the new EP they were promoting that night.

No sooner had I done so than Mark, the guitarist in the band who was hovering nearby, said beamingly, "Oh, Charlie Gitane was in a few minutes ago and he bought one!"

I grinned back. "Yeah? Good stuff." As had always been the case, people frequently mentioned Charlie when they saw me, as though my presence somehow triggered their memory of him. I never knew why this happened but I was starting to find it amusing that it did.

I was momentarily sad I'd missed him but I also deduced that it was probably meant to be. Maybe it would have been too much to come face to face again so soon. Maybe he'd been looking for me. Maybe it had nothing to do with me. I realised that the desperation to see him was fading, turning into a gentle wistfulness. This inner knowing was getting stronger – the knowing that it was all for a reason and if we were meant to meet again, we would. Who was I to try and tamper with the Universe's master plan? And I couldn't, even if I tried. It would only prolong my pain to attempt to steer this thing to my liking. This wasn't something I could grasp from the start, even though I recognised the remarkable work the Universe had done in even bringing us together in the first place. I decided that I'd leave it in the hands of those same cosmic architects. They knew what they were doing. It wasn't always easy to see it that way, but it was getting easier.

It also wasn't easy not to see my acceptance as some form of defeatism. Yet I knew I'd done everything I could to try to allow this love to blossom. That was part of the problem, perhaps. I'd tried way too hard, put all my eggs in one basket and made it all about the relationship, instead of seeing that it was trying to teach me so many other things about myself, about fear and of course about love, about letting things be. How else would I ever have even scraped the underbelly of my fears? Why else would I even have attempted to explore all those shady corners and patched-up wounds? This dance with Charlie had torn those patches off, cast them to the wind and forced me to look. I also learned that looking anything in the eye is actually far less painful than avoiding looking, as long as you look honestly and compassionately. A Universe that could yield a treasure as beautiful as Charlie could likely yield another. I went through my days with this in mind. It might not be Charlie that turns up to share the wonder of the world with me. It could be someone else. It might even be that I'm meant to keep walking alone until I completely understand that happiness can never be dependent on another person, thing or outcome. So, here I sit, in love with this life, still in love with Charlie but open to whatever my path may bring. I wake up each day and know that anything can happen and anything is possible.

Forty-One

Annie and I took a magical trip to Sweden that winter. Even as an adult I get excited by notions of snow, reindeers and elves, so this Scandinavian visit was enchanting from start to finish. We were also lucky enough to see the Aurora Borealis on our last night. This was something truly wondrous for both of us. Although you can read about the scientific phenomena that cause these lights to dance in the sky, they tend to be regarded by most people who actually see them as something awesome and mysterious, not just electromagnetic particles pulsating at a visible frequency in particular latitudes. In medieval times they were seen as signs from the gods and at least in some way, that's what they are to me. Not a sign to tell you such-and-such-a-thing is going to happen, but a reminder that we live in a mysterious and magical Universe that we don't fully understand. Annie and I watched with chattering teeth as the swirling green lights hovered above us. It was faintly eerie at times, but most of all it was magical.

All my life I've been in love with magic and mystery. I'm finally realising that these enchanting wonders are not confined to childhood and fantasy. They accompany us into adulthood to remind us that we don't know it all and we can't solve it all. There's an enormous humility and liberation in that fact. It felt auspicious that we had seen those Northern Lights on our last night in Sweden, and as the spectacle faded we were both honoured to have witnessed such a thing. There are many kinds of lights, which trigger many kinds of mood. There are certain kinds of light that you just can't ignore, or explain, or forget.

We had an unearthly 4am start to get to the airport and catch our flight back to London. I stumbled out of bed and into the shower in pitch darkness, remembering the beauty of the Northern Lights that had crept somewhere into my dreams, even though I couldn't disentangle the details. Groaning a little with disorientation, Annie and I checked out of our hotel, and still undercover of the night we climbed on board a bus that delivered us to another bus headed for the airport. It was at the changeover of buses that something startling happened.

It was when we boarded the airport coach. Annie sat in the window seat and I took the aisle seat. Across the sleepy coach, in another seat, I suddenly – in a flash – saw Charlie… but only for a moment. There he sat, slightly slumped in a coat, running his fingers through his hair. Although he appeared to be flesh and blood he was bathed in a certain kind of light that may have been a reflection of the orange street lights outside as it was still completely dark, but the light that enveloped him reminded me of the Northern Lights. He seemed wrapped up in the sheen of that slightly spooky glow we'd seen dancing above us the night before. It was one hundred per cent him, not a passenger that looked like him, and within about five seconds he was gone again. I turned tremblingly to Annie but stopped myself before explaining what I'd seen, or

278

attempting to explain, not for fear that she'd think I'd truly lost the plot (and I wouldn't blame her if she did), but because she was a nervous flyer and I didn't want to freak her out with reports of apparitions. What had I experienced? Was it real? Had I conjured him up through prolonged desire to see him or had he voluntarily – or involuntarily – popped in from the astral plane? At this early hour back in London he'd probably be still asleep or perhaps about to wake up. I kept my strange vision to myself until we were back home. Of all the strange occurrences of the past few years, this was the first time I'd actually witnessed an apparition of him in a place I *knew* he wasn't. Though I was fascinated, I wasn't scared.

I did tell Annie what I'd seen when the flight was behind us, and was surprised she didn't seem to find it too odd or question my sanity, but then people had been duplicating around us for years now so this was only a *bit* wackier than that. She mentioned she thought something had been up with me on the coach. I told no one else about this because I was secretly becoming a little worried about myself – and about Charlie. Did it mean something was wrong with him? Or was it that something was wrong with me? Could people really flit about astrally in this manner? Did people perhaps do this quite a bit but not normally be seen? Or was I now ready for the doctors to carry me away and knock some sense into me?

I did a small amount of research on the internet and discovered similar things had happened to others, and the likely explanation given was the person seen had been astrally travelling and you just happened to catch their spirit in the act. I knew how frequent and vivid my dreams of Charlie had always been so perhaps it wasn't so strange that I could see him in Sweden when his physical body was more than likely lying in bed in Streatham. Zharha would be the person to tell, the person who would tell me whether I was imagining things – or seeing things as they really can be seen at certain times in certain circumstances.

"You were in a magical, energetic hub," Zharha explained. "This area, along with all of Northern Europe, is the fairy realm. He is your strongest connection and that was bound to come out, being where you were."

I listened, enthralled. So, I wasn't crazy. It was real. It *is* real, though of course my definition of 'real' had been shifting for a long time and was still being regularly challenged. For a short while after this strange vision, I worried it would keep happening – but it didn't. For whatever reason I didn't see him where he wasn't supposed to be any more. Perhaps it was just a little jolt to keep me open to the mysteries of the Universe, to the power of our connection and the magic of it all.

Forty-Two

This morning when I awoke it was as though I had to unwrap myself from multiple layers of sleep, consciously break out of the arms of slumber and move. When I came to view the world outside from the window I gasped a little to see the dense layers of fog that had spun themselves around every physical thing that stood in the yard, every hulk of half-lit house, every sky-reaching tree and chimney. I knew this was speaking to me on some symbolic level. Perhaps it told me that the spiritual world – perhaps represented by the thick fog – was just as real as the physical world, that in fact it could obliterate the physical world.

Or, maybe the message was that it's good not to be able to see it all, and intuitive and visionary as many, if not all of us are, we don't have all the answers. We don't see *all* the details. Things can be obscured and if we can't see a reason why, doesn't mean there isn't one. This made sense to me, as the night before I had made another big surrender. One I hoped to be long-lasting, if not eternal. I'd decided to hand it completely over to the Universe. I don't necessarily know what's best for me. I knew what I wanted and I still wanted Charlie, but I was finally able to accept that the Universe knew better. I could look at my life through a keyhole and glimpse possibilities for my soul, but the Universe could see everything in both broad daylight and the inky darkness of the night. It could see it all and I couldn't.

Heaven knows, I'd asked enough times for help and I couldn't decide whether I needed to keep praying this decade-old prayer or to just stop and accept that whatever was right would eventually happen. I'd surrendered before. I'd been OK with it not happening before. In fact, I still was OK but that prayer had become lodged in my system again on repeat play. I decided that to keep asking was probably tiresome for the Universe. I'd make it clear one more time that was what I desired, but that if something else, something better, or something ultimately right for me was in waiting then I understood and that was fine. I handed all the paperwork over to the angels.

'Paperwork' is too light a term. There were battered box files, tear-stained notebooks, lever arch files bursting with dreams. They'd been weighing me down. They couldn't be chucked away, burnt, deleted – though I did force myself to delete most of his texts and emails, not that we had a prolific correspondence, because we didn't. But last night I handed them over to the angels, who took them away to a different realm, to the realm of out of my hands, which is where everything involving Charlie seemed to live. I'd gone through this before, admittedly. It took me a long while to surrender, but even when I had, I hadn't truly surrendered attachment to the outcome. I'd been scared to do that because I thought if I stopped believing, that might make a resolution unbelievable, unattainable. But where did these beliefs come from? My rules? Universal rules? Someone else's rules?

If I looked closely I could see I was operating from fear, from lack of trust. *Just hand it over*. I'd carried it, nurtured it, cuddled it, washed and cleaned it, made it sparkle and shine. I'd slept with it, dined with it, moved it from house to house, doorstep to gatepost, it lived with me and I lived with it. I didn't know if it would ever leave completely but I had finally come to the conclusion that though I would still dearly love Charlie to be my man – and he still might be and he might not be – one thing was for sure: that goal must be *r-e-l-e-a-s-e-d*. Giving up in this case meant giving up to the Universe. The Universe brought me this man. It could either bring him back or bring him further away, or bring in another. It's not that I felt powerless. I knew I was more powerful than I had previously realised, but this persistent goal of mine, that whisper to my soul, the answer I'd been seeking for so long, was going to have to be kissed goodbye. Not binned, not scrapped, just given back to the skies. That balloon could be released and it would float where it would float with love, with so much love. And it was after this big surrender that I woke to that dense fog and I somehow knew my prayers had been heard – even though I didn't know what the answer was. And that was actually quite exciting. So this is where I wanted to stay – in that wonder and innocence and trust.

Strange things continued to happen, as though trying to guide and inform me. One chilly morning I waited for the bus to the office, as I do most mornings. Nothing special was on my mind as I looked across the road at the letting agents and the Hungry Dragon Chinese takeaway. A thought just popped into my head, a nondescript voice speaking rapidly: *The weekly pass has gone up*. It was as if someone had rushed up and whispered these words in my ear and hurried away again. There was no reason to suspect an increase in bus fares. It wasn't a seasonal thing and certainly no advertising had been visible to pre-empt this. I neither dismissed nor accepted the message, but I clearly heard it as the bus sailed up to the stop. I boarded and asked for my weekly pass.

"It's gone up to sixteen pounds, unfortunately," the driver mentioned as I dug into my handbag for my purse.

"No problem," I exclaimed, with rush of excitement that I'd been sent that information ahead of time

But why – and from whom?

About twenty minutes later, the same sense of knowing, that matter-of-fact voice said, *Charlie is coming back.* I was stunned. It was that matter-of-fact quality that had my attention. It had been exactly the same when I'd been told *Hudson is going to tell you Charlie is getting married* (which of course had happened soon after). It had more to say: *Get ready!* I didn't really know what to think. Perhaps it's not that weird. I mean, it wouldn't be that strange if he came back into my life but I still found it a little shocking. I wasn't asking again either. Had they first spoken to me about the mundane matter of the bus fare to show me they were reliable? Could I trust this information? Although everything told me I could, I guess I didn't want to pin all my hopes on it. Only time would tell.

Later that evening I think about what I heard on the bus. I close my eyes and listen, wondering if perhaps they will speak again. All I can hear is semi-silence... floorboards creak upstairs and a door slams shut next door. A plane tears through the clouds snuggling in the

South London sky. *Can I trust those messages I heard on the bus?* I ask the guides. *That he's coming back? And what exactly does that mean? Was that real?* The silence swirls and no answer comes. Do they only tell me once and then I have to trust it? How long will it be before it happens? A distant siren sounds somewhere around the block. I know. I know that what I have to do is live, be happy and keep on loving. What will be, will be.

The important shift that had occurred was that as much as I still wanted him and still loved him deeply, I knew I could still be happy even if we never met again. Still, my soul continued to reach for him in a way that felt involuntary. The love remained – and remained. When alone, I sometimes found myself involuntarily saying his name. His name remained on my lips, like a drop of vintage wine or mist of morning dew, like part of my being; on some level he *was* part of my being. If a molecule of me was split in two he would be somewhere in the mix, his essence forever mingled with my soul. It didn't seem strange any more. It didn't hurt quite as much any more, but it never was not so. And I also knew I wasn't just connected to Charlie. We are *all* part of each other, but it took what I went through with and without Charlie to show me it really is that way. We're more than flesh and blood and we don't exist in isolation, though it can feel that way if we're out of touch with ourselves. This was no parrot-fashion, New Age fad notion. It was an ancient truth. Charlie had put me back in touch with things that mattered, while things that didn't ceased to bother me. That kind of waking up and shaking up could never be reversed or forgotten.

The information kept filtering through in my dreams. I recall one vivid nocturnal escapade involving making a trip to a postal sorting office to collect an item. The landscape was clearly Victorian, both in terms of the buildings and the feel of the place, though I was dressed in modern clothes. I walked under an arch and up a cobblestoned alley and entered the post office. Charlie was working behind the counter. He was delighted to see me and immediately smiling. Again I could hear his thoughts (though his mouth wasn't speaking), which were, *Oh, great, you came so quickly! I only took this job in the hopes you'd come in*, and he went to get my item for me, which was a boxed parcel. I knew it contained something highly precious.

Thanking him, I went back down the cobbled alleyway but when I was halfway along an astonishing light shone on my path – a big, bright flash hit the ground and I was momentarily glued to the spot whilst having the realisation that this was something I'd dreamt of before (even though I don't think I have consciously). I was also aware of my guides or some higher being, who I couldn't see but could feel as a warm and certain presence.

A chorus of voices spoke, yet they sounded clear and unified, more like one multipartite voice saying, "Remember this, Eileen – you see, dreams do come true!" and I was wrapped in an amazing blanket of bliss. Once I'd got the message and knew it was true, I ran on excitedly down the cobblestoned path with my mysterious gift. I knew the gift was both from him as well as somehow being his very self, and it could be literal or symbolic. Either way, I knew it was priceless. There was past life energy in that dream too. I was very sure we'd had dealings with each other in Victorian times, but it wasn't as simple as a re-enactment of that. I cherished these dreams and the information I was given even if I didn't fully understand it. It wasn't meaningless night-time garbage. When those voices spoke in my dreams I felt so humbled and thrilled I can't even begin to explain the feeling. It was impossible for me not to take these transmissions seriously.

Forty-Three

It's all about love and it's all about fear. You can only have one without the other. If there was a nutshell lesson in all of this it may go along those lines. But fear wears so many disguises, and though it is often the root issue it manifests in all kinds of nasty ways. Fear can be overcome with love, but love can lead to the craziest fear of all. It was easy for me to see Charlie as being afraid, and I had no doubt he was, but my own fears were being mirrored back at me left, right and centre and I failed to recognise this at first. Fear that I wasn't good enough, young enough, beautiful enough, interesting enough – even though on some strange level I knew none of this mattered this time. This time, normal relationship rules were redundant, but that's easier said than done when you bring two people together who have no other reference points than what they've grown up with, who've developed patterns based on past woundings they are barely aware of.

I don't pretend to understand how I developed so many fears but meeting Charlie dragged them to the surface and seemed to demand that they were dealt with. I even had a fear that I'd lose what was seemingly destined. Fear I'd mess it up. Fear I didn't deserve it. Fear I might get it! Fear that it would slip away before it even had a chance. Fear that I was somehow different and would

288

never fit in, or have a normal life or a normal relationship. That perhaps I was some sort of alien that didn't belong and had been thrown here by mistake. It's taken me a long time to see I'm no different from anyone else, no better, no worse, no more special, no less special.

So, these are the days they foresaw, the sunless, freezing fog days, filled with sirens and shopping... the end of an age, the start of another. For years 2012 had been talked and joked about as some important evolutionary landmark or apocalypse. It was about halfway through that year that I became aware that something big *was* going on, something fashioned out of the same bigness that crashed into my life a decade ago. I suppose we could call it raised vibrations. Blog posts and references I read online call it 'the shift'.

I didn't think this shift was anything to do with the world ending but I did get a sense of the world changing in a very major way. This was real. Though keenly aware of the upheaval and chaos in the world right around me, I was also starting to get truly excited at what felt like a real possibility of a better world, a cleaner world, an honest, more loving, more unified world... a *magical* world. Skeletons were spilling out of the closets at alarming rates, people were being challenged and held accountable for old misdeeds and even though it seemed some were still getting away with murder, literally and metaphorically, the overall feeling was *Time's up!* Despite the feeling of the carpet being yanked out from under my feet here and there, I rejoiced at this. Who doesn't want a better world?

Strangely enough, on the eve of the Winter Solstice of 2012 I had a dream. I dreamt I was monitoring a website which appeared as just a big black page with a giant pie chart graphic on it. The pie chart was supposed to illustrate how many people had 'awakened' and how many more needed to before we reached 'critical mass' – that was the term used in the dream – and if we hit it on the 21st December the world would be rebalanced and a new world could take shape. So, I was watching it on a screen late on the 21st December and it looked sadly like we weren't going to make it – but then, at the eleventh hour, the measurement on the chart just tipped over into what was deemed critical mass numbers, causing a riot of red lights to start flashing all over this big console/dashboard that looked like it belonged on a spaceship. As the lights started flashing and beeping noises sounded I was shown the globe – planet Earth spinning in space – and it was lighting up with exquisite colours in every corner. We'd made it! And there was a great feeling of happiness, celebration and excitement.

I still remember that dream and wonder what exactly *is* going on. I don't have the answers but I do have the hopes, aspirations and dedication. We're all in this together because no matter how much we try to fence ourselves off and look out only for our nearest and dearest, that's not going to make the world a better place, that's not going to heal our souls. It takes embracing the whole, because we're all part of the whole – whether we like it or not, whether we see it or not.

A painful pang struck me from out of the blue yesterday as I realised that I really miss Charlie's performances. In the years that he was a regular part of my life I almost took that talent, on stage or screen, for granted. Being an actor

290

was something I assumed he would always be. In the same way that I felt I would always put pen to paper, he would surely always keep exploring and inventing characters, speaking words like magic phrases that could open doors, channelling that soul energy in a direction that felt so right, so good, so intrinsically him. I had to stop and catch myself when that loss hit me.

A deep sadness spread through my body and my eyes welled up with tears. Charlie, and to some extent the collective of the Last Exit Players, had provided a beautiful theatrical landscape to the most recent decade of my life and I'd always thought that if not the entire group, then at least Charlie would continue to enrich my world with his sweet, sweet smile. It's been several years now since he's worked properly in theatre. Does he still wish to? Does he still read scripts? Does he miss the stage? The rise and fall of the curtains? The applause? The creative buzz that kind of work brings? I truly wonder how such a creative person can appear to put out the fire. Yet, I also know it isn't completely put out. It smoulders. I know he does still tread the boards of the stage on some level as I've seen him in my sleep. He could have a stash of plays under his pillow. All I know is, I believe in him. I love him, whatever he chooses to do with his life. I would just love to share our lives again. I miss his voice, his presence, his humour, his eyes, his hair, his slightly crooked mouth, the touch of his hand, but I know somehow he's not that far away. Wherever he is, I feel him still.

Forty-Four

A Monday night. I slip beneath the covers and hug my arms around my shoulders to gather together some warmth. A clap of thunder sounds outside, and another… and another… a barrage of hail batters the windowpane. I can even hear the snap, crackle and pop sound effects falling down the chimney which resides in the wall behind my bed. I listen in absolute peacefulness.

The drama out there in the night can't impinge on me. I feel safe, warm, in the sanctuary of my bed. This is how I want to be regarding emotional drama, I decide. All I needed to do was step into the eye of the storm. There was a place of stillness that I could step into and though I would see the rain pour before my eyes like a towering waterfall, I could stand just inside that place, where I'd be sheltered from the storm. Tonight, I've found that place of refuge. I need to step inside here more often. I know now that if Charlie does come back into my life on a regular basis I'll no longer be buffeted about by the emotional waves. It hasn't happened so I can't be sure it won't knock me off my feet again – but one thing I have learnt is that I can choose my response. I can't stop the love and I don't want to, but I can sail my ship towards the shore with quiet contemplation and steady breathing. Being balanced isn't being boring. I no longer need drama to make me feel alive. I've never felt more alive than when I'm still and quietly aware, like right now, listening to the hail dissolving into rain, pitter-pattering throughout the night.

Wednesday evening, I sat on the upper deck of a bus driven by a reckless driver determined to get to the depot ahead of time. Daylight was dissolving into darkness as we tore through Clapham, and as I looked from the window at the blackening clouds huddling closer I experienced a moment likely to stay with me, a moment that proved I was something more than a bunch of bones, flesh and clothing speeding through a South London suburb in late February.

It was as though the transformation of dusk into darkness was happening molecule by molecule, and I could actually see this energy pooling together to become something almost solid. That shift from semi-light to semi-dark and to darker still is a gradual process that happens every day and it's near impossible to pinpoint its stages. What I was catching or observing that evening felt extraordinary. It was as though something physical was manifesting, and on some level I felt it was personal. It was like an acceleration of all my thoughts, hopes, dreams and beliefs gathering together to take form and shape, to turn into *things*! I could feel it, like some huge cosmic vessel was pouring an accumulation of patterns into a mould that would set overnight and become a recognised shape by the morning. I felt excitement, but also confusion. Was I creating or being created? Was I conjuring this up or was I simply witnessing? I didn't know. Was I creating this materialising yet ethereal substance, this merging of palpable but invisible particles?

Then I heard them: the guides. They hadn't spoken for a while but they delivered the same message: *Get ready!* I waited for more, and more came. Just two words: *Be strong.* There was that sound when they spoke, like the trees were leaning towards me and the wind rustled their leaves and whispered in my ear. I continued to listen in case there was more. I did my best to listen without pre-empting, without implanting my thoughts into the situation, just being as receptive as possible. This seemed to be all that was coming verbally, but there was a feeling that had accompanied the message, a feeling of enormous strength, of vitality, of power. Even though I'd had a long day and was previously tired I felt invigorated and excited. I noted they hadn't mentioned Charlie, or Charlie coming back, but then, they had already delivered that message, so why repeat it, I reasoned? Whatever it was that I needed to be ready for, they had let me know I had the strength to see it through, to handle it. I'd jumped off the bus, and walked purposefully down Balham Station Road. I felt almost ecstatic, invincible. I didn't understand what was firing me up but it was a wonderful way to feel, and perhaps it was simply an awareness of who I really am, how vast and wonderful we all are when we shed the ego and allow ourselves to just be.

When I got indoors, excitement grew even more when I glimpsed a fox disappearing onto Bedford Hill. This doesn't sound remarkable, other than the fact that foxes as well as black cats had followed Annie and me all over London when we first arrived, and had continued to for several years. We both felt they had some mystical power and meaning and would gasp in wonder when one revealed itself at a particularly significant moment. The foxes had suddenly stopped appearing some years ago (the cats continue to do so, but perhaps that's not so strange, cats being common in most parts). Now we almost never saw foxes locally, yet one had showed tonight.

"He must have followed you up to the gates," Annie remarked as the security lights in the car park had come on moments after I'd pulled shut the door and entered the kitchen. We both watched the car park beneath our window for another glimpse of the bushy tail, the enchanting fox, but a glimpse was all there was. Glimpses are sometimes all you get – like the glimpse of the mechanics of the Universe I'd had on the bus that evening. A glimpse, though, is sometimes all we can handle, and is still a reality, if we catch it, if we recognise it.

Forty-Five

Nothing but blue skies in early March! I step out to post my Mother's Day card with bucketloads of love. Next, I buy a takeaway flat white from my favourite coffee shop and go home to sip it before immersing myself in writing. I can't believe how good I feel. I can't believe how flexible and happy my joints feel. I'm squatting on the floor so I can keep an eye on the toast browning under the grill, staring up through the high windows at the azure acres of sky stretching for miles and miles. I suddenly realise I am healed. It still amazes me when I have this realisation, almost as though I have no right to feel this good – to feel this good just to be alive. I immediately start giving thanks to the Universe for everything in my life: all the wonderful people, my health, my happiness, the food I'm about to eat, the coffee I'm sipping. Everyone I encountered when I stepped out earlier was smiling and seemed pleased to see me. I felt I wanted to share this feeling of simplicity and true happiness. What I understood now is that my happiness wasn't dependent on anything other than my choosing it. I thought about Charlie. I loved him just the same. I still wanted to see him, to be with him, but his absence in no way diminished my joy.

Being me one hundred per cent was like a new sensation, like I'd re-bolstered myself, re-sprung;

returned my energy to where it belonged, creating a huge surge of me! I'd read about how these kind of experiences with strong soul connections were about finding yourself ultimately, and though I'd definitely glimpsed the real me repeatedly through the last decade it was mainly in his eyes – that magic reflection that you may try to blink away, but though it's a real reflection, a reflection isn't something you can ever capture and a glimpse just isn't enough. I didn't want to be a spectre of myself any more. I wanted to be who I was, and who I was could stand alone or alongside him – or anyone else – without getting sucked up, made small, made out of shape or out of rhythm, without losing myself in the process of trying to find love. I know where love lives. This was about becoming rock solid to the core by reclaiming my spirit, contradictory though that sounds.

So many times I'd wrestled with who I truly was, feeling different, weird, perhaps even a freak but when you realise that nobody else can define you or malign you, that you know who you are and you're happy about it, then, that worry about what anybody else thinks just falls away. I'd given away my power time and time again and left myself precious little to keep my engine running. I wasn't even seeing myself body and soul as the miracle we all are, but once you begin to see YOUR SELF as sacred, you realise if you aren't honouring yourself nobody else can. It's not about ego. It's all about love and being comfortable in your own skin. We're drowning in throwaway, mass-produced self-help phrases and books these days. These so called instructions for living mean nothing until you stand face to face with your true self and befriend that being, until you put down the book, switch off the computer and discover the joy of simply being alive and being yourself and making no apologies for it.

I realise how nauseatingly upbeat all this could sound, but there must be a reason this all happened, and I'm telling it. I wanted people to know what I'd discovered, and weaved it into the screenplay for *Une Lumière Particulière*:

> *Even if you meet someone that you share a profound soul connection with, or whatever label you want to give or not give to a person who you love inside out and more than words can say, a person that nestles up to your soul and whispers to you so softly it makes you melt, you meet them, you fall for them, you ache for them with a hunger that it seems nothing else can ever satisfy — I want people to know that tragic as it seems, if they don't choose to be with you, all your love is not in vain. You can turn it inside out and learn to love yourself and LIFE itself. It's a convoluted journey but it's not the cruel cosmic joke you may have mistaken it for when you felt like you were crawling along a dust trail, when you nearly collapsed at the deserted crossroads with no signs, no birds, no music, no sun, no moon… none you could see or hear… at that point. If that's where you are now, please, please trust and surrender. You will come out the other side. And you never know who might be waiting there for you.*

These were words I wrote passionately into the script. It had become the story of Charlie and me, and though I worried about his reaction if he ever went to see the film I knew the story had to be told.

I used to count the weeks between seeing him. Lately it's been more a case of counting months. Perhaps it will soon be years. I don't know. I was aware it had been a long time now since we re-bonded in Hudson's Cave. In fact it had been five months. As far as I recall this is the longest stretch of time encountered without at least a fleeting meeting. Yet, this time I wasn't worried it wouldn't happen; I wasn't even counting. I'd had multiple signs and dreams that something was truly stirring in this situation. Night after night, he'd drop by or I'd drop by, and my duvet felt crumpled, ruffled affectionately by his visit in the nicest possible way. Sometimes we had long conversations, sometimes I merely observed him in situations that I felt were meant to tell me something. He might be performing onstage, or there was one very recently involving him in a hallway, grabbing his coat and keys, pulling shut a front door and running. Running. Running away in escape mode or running towards a goal?

Yet, we eluded each other in earthly physical life, day after day, which is probably why I wondered about the relevance of the constant signs and dreams. I knew they symbolised positive shifts, I knew they were real on some level. They were gifts for me, sometimes straight from his heart, sometimes from the Universe, sometimes from me to myself. I knew I wasn't 'making them up' for they constantly enthralled me with the richness of their metaphors and messages. I never knew what was coming and they were just too fascinating and puzzling to have been invented purely by me, though obviously some part of me was responsible for my part in them. When Charlie and I spoke in many of these dreams I had no doubt we truly were conversing. I could hear his voice, his vernacular, his pauses and his inner thoughts, though not always. His body language replicated itself perfectly on the astral plane.

It was the day before I was due to travel to Manchester to visit an old friend who was sadly getting divorced. I was going to offer any support and comfort I could. I sat at work the day before my trip, feeling overwhelmed with this recent energy, this big, swirling dance of the gods that I didn't really understand but accepted I was invited to. Suddenly I found myself asking the big assembly in the sky, the Universe, whoever was responsible for all this to give me a sign that I wasn't making all this up, that it was real, and a sign in the physical world, preferably straight from Charlie himself, because much as I did trust the dreams and the synchronicities, the messages in songs that tapped me on the shoulder all the time, I'd had an absolute abundance of these and nothing on the earthly plane for months. I asked if it was possible, could I have a flesh-and-blood-type sign? Please? I was aware this was perhaps a little cheeky of me but at the same time, my soul was confused. Strong though I was on most days, I needed *something*.

After asking, I forgot all about it. I had a lot on my mind – family concerns, travel arrangements, an application form for a new position that had arisen at a publishing house I was interested in. I'd ordered a taxi to Euston station because I had an early train to catch and quite a bit of luggage. I wasn't in the mood for dragging things round. I knew I was shedding my karmic baggage; all that long-term psychic junk was being washed down the drain every day like suds in the shower, and lugging around physical baggage seemed equally inappropriate.

The taxi driver was complaining crossly about the government. I agreed with him, as we swung round onto Euston Road and swept past Euston Tower and the pathway to Camden. Then suddenly his words concerning David Cameron disappeared from my radar as I saw Charlie and Danielle walking rapidly along Euston Road towards the station.

In a big station like this we would probably not bump into each other, I told myself, knowing full well that we would. I paid the driver and exited the taxi. Once inside the station I began to scan the bewildering departures board. Out of the corner of my eye, I sensed, then saw Charlie and Danielle at the entrance of the ticket office to my left. I didn't turn to look and stayed glued to the screen, but somehow I couldn't see my train. Next thing I knew Danielle walked right across my path. I could tell from her unhappy, tight-lipped expression she had clocked me. This time I didn't feel the same toxic charge I normally did – it was as though she was still emitting it but I was somehow neutralising it, catching it in mid-air before it could attack me. She walked on, and I didn't look to see where.

Within seconds, Charlie crossed my path too. "Hello, Eileen." There it was, that same soft, loving tone. He literally hung in front of me for a moment, unsure of whether to walk on or stop and talk.

"Hello. How are you?" I said, and we both indicated we were fine. I wanted to talk more but I was worried I might delay him – perhaps he was rushing for a train. He hesitated in the same way. Then he walked on and I was left still scanning the board, which was just a swirling pool of letters and numbers that may as well have been written in another language.

It was so good to see him, even for that one moment. I felt lighter and suddenly animated. I finally found which platform my train was leaving from, and headed towards a food outlet to buy a coffee, pulling myself together and finding my focus. I still had a little while before the train was ready for boarding. It felt odd standing there at the gate waiting to get on the platform, still with the golden, sun-kissed feeling of Charlie mingling with my aura. Next thing I knew, I felt a voice from behind, a slightly hesitant and a gentle greeting.

"Hello?" It was intoned as a semi-question, as though asking, *Can I come in?*

I turned around, knowing who was speaking but barely believing it until I saw his eyes. "Hello!"

There he was, armed with coffee and croissants, clearly no defence against the current that was drawing us together in the same way it always had. We talked and talked. It was both small talk and big talk. He was actually travelling on the same train as me, though only one stop to Watford, for a work-related meeting. By the end of our conversation, a few things were clear to me. He cared. He still cared and he was still my special companion. He was healing on some level. I could feel it and hear it in his words. He spoke of giving up smoking, cutting down on drinking and also, most importantly, returning to his acting, dusting off some old scripts, re-examining his direction and hopefully reigniting that creative part of his life that he clearly missed so much. I missed it so much too. I also felt tender support from him to me. He was sympathetic about my friend I was going to see. We didn't touch each other physically in any way – since he'd gotten engaged, touching had automatically stopped – but by time we parted I felt I'd been hugged, a deep soul hug. We were both planning on going to see Black Rebel Motorcycle Club when they played that weekend, when I was back from Manchester, so we parted on that note, that we might see each other soon.

It was after he'd gone I realised my request from the day before had been granted. I'd witnessed that physical manifestation of the stuff that had been building invisibly for so long. Things were getting so much better. All those months where he wouldn't speak, wouldn't meet, wouldn't respond had simply melted away. I knew we could be friends again. We *were* friends again. For once, I didn't need to make it more than that. I didn't need to inject romance into the equation. I didn't need to be his girlfriend, wife or lover. I was happy to be his friend – even though I knew we could be everything to each other, we could match and complement each other on any level. This love was so vast, it washed the whole platform clean, it flowed through each carriage on the train. It was our love, but it was bigger, bigger, *bigger* than us. We were just a part of the whole. I understood that now.

I watched him get off the train at Watford Junction and my soul didn't pine after him. It blessed him. It admired him. It kissed him with a love-infused snowflake on his forehead, lingering for a moment and then letting him go on his way. How long had it taken to get to this amazing place where I could hold that love in my heart but not have to possess him? A long time, a hard time, but a worthwhile time most definitely.

I must admit, it was helpful with going into a sad situation with my sweet friend to have had that fleeting encounter with dear Charlie. It somehow gave me strength, gave me energy to face whatever I had to face when in Manchester. I did what I could when there and tried to help mop up any pain I could. Yet, you can't take someone's pain away, though sometimes being with them, sitting with them can offer a grain of comfort.

On my way home an unexpected drama occurred. I'd been dropped by my mum and sister at Stockport train station. I don't know how it happened but as I was making my way up the staircase to my platform I suddenly, without warning or apparent cause, took a tumble and fell forward, dropping my luggage, which slid back down the stairs behind me. I scuffed my hands and somehow bashed my head on the wall. Within a minute or so I realised my head was bleeding as a warm trickle of blood crept down my forehead.

Back in London a few hours later I found myself in A&E waiting for the gash to my head to be examined. Luckily it didn't look too serious and a kind doctor gave me some dissolvable stitches and a tetanus shot. Dizzily, I lay in bed that night with the drama of the day flashing before my eyes, as well as my friend's pain. I also remembered Charlie and the softness of the interaction at the station, a real contrast to the journey back. I eventually fell into fluttery, fleeting dreams of little substance. I was strong enough to cope with all this. Thank God I'd healed enough to know that.

Forty - Six

Even whilst descending the red velvet, well-worn staircase, I could feel it. That sense of knowing Charlie was near. I didn't take too much notice of it, to be honest. I'd enjoyed the gig, despite a sea of strange energy that was hurling itself against the walls – a mild panic, a confused discordance. Was it just because my head injury was making me extra-sensitive? Was it just because I knew there was a good chance he was in the building? Was it just because he *was* in the building? Because she was? Because they were? Was it just because I'd had that beautiful encounter on the platform and I was worried something would arise to contradict it? Or worried something would occur to amplify it? Could I handle it? It was absurd to feel this way, but feel this way I did. *I don't want to feel this way any more. I want to keep my energy even. I want to learn to have no fear. It's about learning to know the difference between an impulse of self-preservation and fear... or do they both come from the same ugly root?* That's something I was still grappling with.

Annie and I exited Shepherds Bush Empire and paused with a sea of people waiting to cross the road. It was as though some intuitive text alert had been transmitted, causing me to turn my head dutifully to the left, and a short distance away I saw Charlie and Danielle also waiting to cross the road. The Universe had done another nifty job of engineering a same-place-same-time potential rendezvous. It's against the odds at a large public event to run into the one person you're hoping (on some level) to see. Had Charlie been alone I'm almost certain I would have risen to the occasion, waved, made contact, had a chat, maybe even gone for a drink, but the moment I saw Danielle at his side I wanted to withdraw from the opportunity. I'd made that decision in a split second: I wanted to hide, to run. Here it was again, that inexplicable urge to run from someone you hold so dear. The person you've been dying to see in so many ways. But there I was, ducking behind the crowd, asking Annie to hold back a moment until they'd crossed the road. I hadn't experienced the urge to hide from him for a while, not since that odd near-encounter on the train on the way back from Reading.

So did this mean I still had stuff to deal with? I thought I was doing so well. I think perhaps I was more unwilling than incapable of handling a close encounter. I could foresee how it would go. Danielle would glare at me, and Charlie would either wink, wave or grin – or exhibit some compensatory behaviour for her unfriendliness. Not that I had any problem with his behaviour. Or perhaps his behaviour was nothing to do with her. Perhaps he would have surprised me. Perhaps she would. Perhaps I should have found out. I think maybe I was still a little fragile from the bash on the head in Stockport and was just trying to protect myself. Luckily the crowds populating the street as the venue continued to spew out its audience made hiding easy – or so I thought, though perhaps I had already been spotted. If I could detect his presence like a scent, it made sense he could do the same.

I'm aware I've overanalysed the situation here too. It's time to just let it go. I missed a chance to see dear Charlie. I can live with that. Life is full of beautiful things and so many opportunities are missed, not just simple greetings like this. I decided I wanted to embrace life and everything in it more, to appreciate each moment. I told myself as Annie and I went home on the bus that I'd step up next time. *If I don't want him to run from me I mustn't run from him, but for now, let it go. Let it go, like the traffic climbing towards the Westway into the night.*

After that particular fleeting rendezvous with Charlie the dreaming seemed to accelerate yet again. There were big, epic dreams, snatched snippet dreams, long, rambling journeys and peculiar half-in/half-out dreams where I knew I was awake but I hadn't shut the door to the other realm – or he hadn't – and I could literally lie on my mattress and see a passageway of light between us. If I peered down this portal I knew he was there, and if I reached out my hand it was almost as though I could touch him. I often saw his face lying sideways on a pillow, staring back at me – sometimes looking vacant, sometimes engaged and actively watching. Sometimes I'd talk to him a little. Sometimes I'd just close my eyes and snuggle up to the warm channel of love that seemed to flow from my flat in Balham to wherever he was, which I assumed was the flat he shared with Danielle a couple of miles away from mine in Streatham, in the real world. The 'real world' was a phrase I'd begun to use with a grain of salt.

Sometimes the dreams were a comfort, sometimes a

surging excitement, sometimes just an intriguing puzzle, sometimes a torment or worry. I'd wake with a start and be so chuffed that we'd just had a chat, a dance of energy, an exchange that felt just like it used to in the 'real' world. Sometimes there'd be a tinge of sadness – he'd have a troubled look on his face, or he'd be distressed, following me round like a small child in striped pyjamas. There was a lot of following each other around in the dreams. Usually, if I was following him it would be through winding streets, through crowds, through drinking dens, up or down stairways. On the contrary, when he followed me it tended to be from room to room, in a domestic setting.

I'd discussed the intensity and frequency of the dreams with Zharha. She confirmed, from her perspective, that these dreams were definitely shared and that Charlie was actively participating in them, willing them, looking forward to them. Although this was nice to hear in many ways and I knew I enjoyed those nocturnal trips together too, the earthly side of me wanted more, wanted a flesh-and-blood relationship – and by that I don't necessarily mean it had to be a sexual relationship.

The thing was, many of these dreams, especially the sexual ones, felt astonishingly real and it bothered some part of me that we were having this astral affair whilst back in the real world he was married to someone else and we had very little contact these days. How could it be? How could it *not* be? How could it stop? How could it carry on? I was confused and growing impatient, wishing for the dreams to manifest on the earthly plane. If he really was hanging out with me in that other world as often as it seemed, loving me the way he did in the dreams, why the hell wasn't he turning up on my doorstep with a bunch of roses and saying, "OK, let's carry on in real life!"? That's what I wanted to happen, but he wasn't showing up. I'd not seen him for months again at this point. Was I being taken for a ride? Was he happy having an affair on the astral plane, and that satiated him? Did he not *want* to make it real? What *was* real? Was it already real and I was the one that was mistakenly fixated on what *appeared* to be real in the three-dimensional everyday world? I was still struggling with understanding what all this soul stuff is made of – the fact that we are multidimensional. If our souls are immortal and our souls love each other, then why wouldn't they behave as his and mine were? Perhaps it wasn't part of the plan to also share this connection physically? Perhaps it was. I knew by now the time had to be right if we were going to come together on all levels, and clearly it still wasn't. It was back to surrender mode and return my focus to myself. This was the only healthy option.

Forty – Seven

I'd done a lot of reading on soul connections and discovered a lot of what I considerd to be nonsense as well as useful information on the subject. I'd also had a few consultations with people who did and didn't call themselves experts in the field, other than Zharha. Again, these consultations I found helpful and others not so much. I'd reached a point, however, where the information became confusing and contradictory and it was time to just let go of all the theories and stop the endless searching. Whatever Charlie was to me, it was a powerful connection and the strangest I'd ever known. He had reflected a light back to me that I now knew could be found inside myself as well as in his eyes, and it was a light that did all sorts of wondrous things and drew us to each other in both physical and non-physical realms. That energy is like the yin/yang circle of perfection, the creative impulse which translates to life itself. What can be more exciting than that?

No wonder when we glimpse even a fraction of that glory we feel like we've been fast-tracked to heaven. But to call any other person your other half or twin soul is ultimately misleading, I now felt, even if it seems the only way to explain the phenomenon. I knew that hot, dream-heavy summer that my challenge was to let go of that idea now. It had served me for a while. It had been a comfort in dark hours when I needed to cling to reasons, an explanation of the absurdity of how inextricable our bond seemed to be. Even the enormity of him getting married hadn't killed the spark like I thought it would or should. It wasn't a mistake to recognise that energy in another, another who matches the energetic fibre of your soul so astonishingly beautifully, but it was limiting to feel trapped by the connection, and it was time to expand my soul, not constrict it.

There was something in the air. It was about a week since that last dream of him. The heatwave we'd all been basking in for the whole month of July had finally broken and gallons of water burst forth onto parched lawns and pavements. It wasn't frustration that had driven me to renew my resolve to let go. It was simply that I had found the courage to accept that he might never be ready and that life was too precious to hang around. Unlike times before in the past when I'd attempted to do this, which were usually fuelled by frustration or anger or some such motivating emotion, what was different here was that the motivation was pure love for myself, for the preciousness of my life. So, I was determined. I wasn't going to block him on the astral plane; I wasn't going to tell him (telepathically) what I was doing or why I was doing it. I wasn't going to employ any psychological rituals like writing a letter and burning it and scattering the ashes in the gardens and backyards of Balham. This time I was just going to do it. I *was* doing it.

I'm still doing it.

Do I have a right to feel this happy? For no obvious

reason... or is there a reason? The truest happiness tends to be non-specific because the minute there's a reason, there's a reliance on certain details being in place. I could list the reasons for feeling happy right now if I wanted to go into my usual analytical mode – the sun is shining this morning, the flowers are blooming, people are smiling, dogs and cats I pass on the street are adorable, music is wafting from windows – it's heavenly, but I also know that warm happiness I'm feeling, that sense of peace, is coming from within. As I weave through my yoga class, stretching, swinging and reaching into crevices I barely registered were part of my anatomy, I feel it – it's like sunshine has slid into every cell in my body, trickling deliciously through each capillary so that even though my back's a bit stiff, my liver's a little congested, I feel so good just to be alive and to finally allow myself that feeling.

For so long I've indulged in drama and struggles that served no real purpose, sometimes out of habit, sometimes because I believed it had to be hard and I couldn't feel good unless certain conditions were met, and that everyone else I loved was as happy as me. Now I'm slowly learning that even though it's good and right to want everyone and everything to be joyous and in alignment, making it so is out of my control and I can only control my own dial, which is currently cranked up to open-armed bliss – for no reason other than that I feel the love, the love from above. Call it the Universe, call it God, call it Source, call it what you will, but it's the same eternal energy that connects us all, nourishes us all, and most wonderfully, is available to every single one of us, if we choose to let it in.

Did it take meeting Charlie and going through those

drawn-out doldrums, those highs, lows and occasional plateaus, to truly grasp this seemingly simple conclusion? For me, maybe it did, maybe it didn't, and simple though it may be, it takes looking at the world through the eyes of the soul, leading with your heart, not your ego, before the impact of that simplicity can be truly felt. It can't be theoretical, it has to be one foot in front of the other and walk – step by step, heartbeat after heartbeat, sun after moon, life after more life. I'm sure I won't (and don't) feel happy every hour of every day. There has to be a balance and we need the rain to fall just as much as we need the sun to shine, but the crucial thing is, I know how to find my way to peace, or at least how to move in the right direction. I know I can be happy and that sunshine may dip behind the clouds here and there, but it's still there, just waiting for us to spot it again. The thing now is to choose this radiance, to live in it and to spread it far and wide.

Forty-Eight

I hadn't seen Charlie for the longest time… over a year, but that was absolutely alright. At points I asked myself if perhaps this was it – I'd never see him again. I'd learned my lesson and so as far as the karma dealers were concerned, there was no reason. Yet, somehow I still had that feeling that we had something I could only define as a future, nebulous though that term is. It's just that my job was to stay focused in the present and that's what I attempted to do. That was the path to happiness. That was the only place to be.

One weekend Annie and I took a detour through the Richmond area on our way back from somewhere else. We were looking for a place to get fish and chips because we were starving and didn't feel like cooking. It was a Sunday evening, a rather dull and colourless close to the week. None of the takeaways we passed were open, but for some reason as we drove along the main road of the town and I glimpsed some of the unknown, twisting streets that unravelled from the main artery of Richmond town, I had an urge to explore and maybe have a walk by the river that we also saw silently flowing in the autumnal twilight. We mentioned we might do that at some point and drove back towards our neck of the woods, which was still Balham.

I forgot about Richmond for the rest of the week,

but like clockwork, when the next weekend arrived, a thought popped into my head instructing me to take a trip over there. Accompanied by the thought was a flash of golden light, so brief and fleeting that I barely tied the two together. Annie suggested a walk and I suggested Richmond, matter-of-factly. It wasn't a burning desire, it wasn't a compulsion, it wasn't anything other than what felt like a totally natural step, an unarguable impulse that I didn't analyse. Strangely enough, Annie didn't question it either. The weekend before had been a prelude of some sort and within an hour or so we found ourselves excitedly rambling around the streets of Richmond, cutting across the green and under an old Tudor arch that we learned was the remains of Richmond Palace.

We explored the area, remarking on all kinds of odd things that seemed to cross our path: black cats, peculiar signposts and a poster outside an old church building that said, *Welcome back. You've been here before*, which we laughed at because fragments of familiarity littered our path with every turn we took. We'd been here before. We were back. As we walked along the Thames, I was struck by the beauty of everything I saw. The world was draped with a certain kind of light. The magic came spiralling along beside us, carried in the water and on the wings of birds. Perhaps it was simply because we were walking through a quaint, Olde Worlde-style area with its feet planted firmly in the past, or perhaps it was simply because we *were* walking through our past – or our past from another lifetime. Either way, the environment was stirring up feelings I couldn't explain and Annie seemed tuned into it too, even though we'd never physically walked this way before.

It reached a point where I had to stop and lean on a stone wall overlooking the mighty river and just catch my breath – not because I was out of puff but just because I was overwhelmed with the energy. It was so beautiful and all I could do was stare at the sun dancing laughingly on the water as it swept along on its way – to where? And where were we going?

Ahead of us at a distance we could see an old seventeenth century pub, and not far from it I also saw an immediately familiar figure. It was Charlie. It *was* Charlie, I knew it, but I told myself I was hallucinating... yet a mild urge to flee began to arise. We kept walking and as we got nearer there could be no doubt it was him, yet Annie hadn't noticed as she was remarking on the beauty of some swans that had appeared on the river.

I muttered, "It's Charlie", wanting to scoot across the road and run away, but it was too late – he was almost upon us and he looked just as surprised as we were.

Bam! Here was the man in the flesh, every bit as handsome as I remembered. There was something majestic about the whole scene – the sweep of the river, the curve of the path, the wideness of the sky and the depth of my love – majestic as we ever were and are. It was like he'd floated out of my dreams – our dreams; *those* dreams – but this was the real world and I knew if I touched him he'd be one hundred per cent flesh and blood. Except no: that's *not* what he is, not what I am, or anyone else – there's more of us in other dimensions than the physical; there's more to us, there's more for us, there's *more*, and it's bigger. Yeah, yeah, yeah.

Charlie wasn't alone. Trundling happily along with him was a little boy aged about three or four.

"Fancy meeting you here!" exclaimed Charlie.

"I know!" I also exclaimed. "Do you live round here?" I no longer knew where Charlie lived, it had been so long since we'd had contact, but I was aware he and Danielle had moved from Streatham.

"No!" Charlie retorted, as though living in Richmond or Twickenham was an impossibility. "Just visiting friends. Say hello, Micky. Say hello to my friends," he instructed the little boy.

I was a swirl of happy if nervous energy. I said hello to Micky and he stared at me silently, as small kids often do with strangers. I don't really know what we said. Annie spoke too but I don't remember any words other than that I told Charlie we'd been for a walk by the river from Richmond and how beautiful the scenery was. He agreed, and by this point little Micky was attempting to run ahead along the path Annie and I had just stepped from, which left no choice but for Charlie to run after him.

"We're going to look for a heron." He grinned. There was that grin I loved.

He moved on smilingly and I called, "I hope you find him!"

"Oh my God!" I repeated quietly as Annie and I crossed over the road towards the seventeenth century pub, and I stood marvelling at the architecture, keenly aware that Charlie and Micky were coming back again, from a rapid glance across the road. Annie and I slipped into the pub and decided to have a coffee, which we'd been planning anyway, and as I sat staring at a menu of swimming words I could barely read I attempted to gather myself back together. How had the Universe engineered this – and why? It was that same old feeling, that wonderful, magical feeling, and I felt a happiness that seemed to spring from my core, from the shared energy, from the wonder of whatever this was that was still undoubtedly there, no matter that we'd hardly spoken, no matter that almost two years had passed since we'd laid eyes on each other – no matter what, it was whatever it was and whatever it was, I loved.

For the rest of the day I sensed that electricity in the air, and my soul smiled like it hadn't in a while. He hadn't disappeared entirely from my life after all. He hadn't disappeared from my heart at all, and something told me that brief exchange had lifted him too, lifted us up where we belonged. But could we stay there?

Forty-Nine

These days I find myself spending a lot of time just staring at light, being mesmerised by the beauty of certain *kinds* of light. Before my front window, a huge, majestic horse chestnut tree stands; its branches tickle the sky and canopy the pavement and the sunlight waves and beckons through those branches, smiling softly, caressing the leaves, kissing the spaces between each outstretched arm. I could watch the light play on the tree for hours. I also watch in wonder through my back kitchen window as the descending sun sets the terraces on fire.

Light – those swirling particles of energy, which in certain circumstances align to create an interplay of energetic frequencies that when hit upon, on rare and stunning occasions, create a certain kind of bliss. I'm no physicist but I know there is a correlation between light and love and he and I. I don't have to understand it. That doesn't mean it doesn't have a massive impact on me, or him, or any of us.

The need to keep surrendering what we can't control is still something I have to remind myself of, but even that's so much easier now because whenever I do, the sense of liberation is instant and beautiful. Early one October morning, as I still lay in bed I had a sudden realisation about the whole thing. I'm not sure if I was being told this or if I just knew it, but I was aware, with no doubt whatsoever, that the love between us just *is*. It's just there, as constant as the sun or sky, and no amount of worrying, wondering, wishing, fearing or obsessing is going to make it more or less. It wasn't a case of trying to fix something, because nothing is broken. The love is there and love causes no pressure or panic, it simply exists. Why was I always looking for confirmation? Why was I always looking to him to tell me or show me? Why was I always waiting for something to happen? It was already happening. Love has happened, is happening and will keep happening.

In my dreamy state, I found myself floating towards a doorway, a big, arched two-door entrance that had white doors with frosted blue handles and frame. I floated towards it and nudged it slightly, not sure if it would open or even if I was supposed to enter. It happily embraced me and I floated inside, and then I could see myself inside, lightly standing on my feet. It looked like the interior of a big cathedral with high, arched ceilings, but there were no statues or furniture that I could see. Huge beams of multicoloured light were bouncing off the walls like lasers and my mouth fell open in awe when I realised this was all made out of love, the energy was love, and it was so powerful, so high in vibration that I could only stand it for a few moments before floating back out of the cathedral and into my body. Was that what divine love was? Is that what divine love is? I was tingling all over, and so excited. What was so exciting was that I knew it was always there. I didn't have to worry about anything because I was loved. I was so loved. I *was* love. So, I didn't need to ask anyone to love me, or go looking for it, as it was right there and not confined to that non-religious cathedral... that kind of love can never be confined. Was this what it was all about? Reaching this realisation? I didn't know, but I was happy and for the first time in a long time I wasn't seeking anything.

This had nothing and everything to do with Charlie. I wasn't dependent on him for anything. I was whole and complete and had a never-ending source of soul sustenance to tap into that had nothing (and everything) to do with him. He had access to it too. We all do. I never stopped wanting him in my life, by my side, in my arms, but after years of struggle to try and somehow make it happen I'd found a whole new vantage point and I could see he was never far away, and if he wanted to cross that cloud, push in that door, and shout with delight when the lasers of love danced around him too, then we could watch them together. Wasn't that the light that had shined from our eyes from the start? That little glimpse of heaven? That spine-tingling, giddy, whooshing, *huge* kind of love?

Let it be! Let everyone see it – if not in another's eyes then through nature, meditation or whatever way it comes to you. Let everyone see that love is not what we often think it is. The trappings of romance can snare your heart, but your heart is so much bigger than the biggest pink balloon you can buy; your soul is so much deeper and delicious than the darkest, richest chocolate you can melt in your mouth. Conventional boy-meets-girl scenarios have been packaged and ingrained on our consciousness for so long that it takes a mighty sledgehammer to smash the mould. Whether you want to call it a soulmate or twin soul doesn't really matter at the end of the day. It happens to smash that old paradigm, to give you the power to create something closer to heaven, something that never limits but expands, that loves unconditionally and empowers us to be the best we can be, that shines such a light that it can be blinding if you aren't ready for it, but once you adapt and see how the landscape's been illuminated there's no going back – and why would you want to go back?

Yes, he was in that dream a few nights back but I can't catch hold of it – it's like a group photo and I know he must have been present because there he is in the picture, but I don't remember him being at the event. I used to feel the need to try and catch the dream, recall any speech, decipher a meaning, hold the memory and energy, but lately there's a tendency to let it float away. He comes and goes – I'll completely forget about it and then at some point in the day, like a very gentle nudge I'll have a fleeting memory of him having dropped by. I could possibly try and claw it back, but it feels unnecessary now. I know that even though he comes and goes, he's always there. I have no need to capture the dreams… or capture his heart.

Last night I dreamt I lived in New York. Magical New York in the snow! Maybe that symbolised the 'new' world, though I know the new world is not far away. All it takes is opening your eyes and choosing it. You *can* choose happiness, but happiness can't choose you! Maybe one day Charlie will join me, maybe he won't. At any rate, I'm done with conformity, superficiality, rigidity, ego games, fear and fakery. Screw the script and talk from the heart! I'm ready for whatever, whoever, wherever is next. Why waste another moment in wondering or worrying? Why waste another precious drop of life in waiting or doing things that don't make you happy? No one knows the future, and I'm glad!

Fifty

After a torrential downpour, the January sun seeped silently back into the picture, setting the roofs on fire. A certain kind of light caught my complete attention and seemed to summon me out of doors. I stepped outside and began to walk up the alleyway and down the street – slowly, gently, lightly. I had no destination in mind. I had no baggage in my hands. I had no pain in my soul. As is often the case after heavy rain, a rainbow was beginning to arch across the heavens. I stopped to admire its spectrum of colour, which continued to intensify and almost solidified. Someone was standing behind me. I could feel their energy field as clearly as I could see the rainbow. I turned around and there was Charlie in a dark winter coat, watching me with faint amusement.

We both stared, then stepped towards each other at the exact same moment, and then he took me in his arms and kissed me.

"Is it really you?" I whispered, aware of the rainbow petrol patterns in the puddle near our feet.

"One hundred per cent," he murmured, holding my face between his palms. Then looking me in the eye, he enquired, "Is it really you?"

"Completely." I grinned, and he grinned broadly back as the winter sunlight danced on the buildings before us.

Maybe this was it. We were whole, we were free. We were love.

I opened my eyes. I knew morning had arrived because I could see the light seeping through the gaps in the curtain. I felt that light expanding quietly. It had a beautiful certainty about it. Daylight had illuminated the neighbourhood outside my window so that all that was hidden by darkness was now visible again. It waited patiently outside as it did every morning. How many times had I barely noticed it and taken it for granted? There it was – expansive, clear and making the whole world perfectly new. My dreams tumbled back into my skull like rocks suddenly scuffling off a cliff. I caught my breath and gasped in amazement. *No, hang on a minute... that... wasn't... a dream. Was it?*

Tremblingly, I got out of bed and made my way downstairs. The door to the kitchen was ajar and I could hear the kettle singing merrily. My heart sang too as I dived straight back into life, into light, into love. Turn on the radio, turn my life upside down; turn the whole thing round... turned out just fine.

Fifty – One

This has been a tale in an atypical typeface, with an itinerary dictated by no clock, or logical full stops. These words were never meant to build a monument to or for Charlie. They're not about anything made of stone. You'll never find God in a statue; you'll never find a soul inside a tomb. No, these words are about breaking hearts of granite, breaking out of the mould, breaking through our defences and pretences and finding what really matters and what's authentic. We're not meant to live on autopilot, as that's not really living. It's time to shatter the slumber that keeps us numbly safe – it's time to dare to love again for me, and to know that I can and I do and I will.

This book isn't going have an ending. It may have a last page but that's just the last thing you'll see before the train bolts into another tunnel and you're plunged into darkness, the last thought you have before sleep suddenly pulls you under and you're no longer aware you're not aware any more. The ending can't really be written because there isn't one. There are conclusions, even amidst the sea of pixelated question marks, breaking up from clumps of ice to pure water, which evaporates, floats on high, falls as rain, snow or hail and hits you with varying levels of pain and pleasure.

The conclusion you draw may not be the same as mine.

Mine may not be the same as it is tomorrow. In terms of how the Universe works, how magic happens, how and why one person can trigger an emotional tsunami in another, well, we just don't have all the answers but I'd hedge my bets that none of it is meaningless coincidence. As physics, philosophy, medicine, mathematics and music begin to waltz to the same universal orchestra, and scientists and priests, doctors, nutritionists, teachers, artists and lovers throw away their obsolete textbooks and dare to take giant leaps of intuition and faith, compassion and respect for the planet and people who walk it, we will be closer to knowing why – but not knowing *exactly* why is what the joy of wonder is made of, and I wouldn't want to lose that.

Today I feel some pain – I feel the pain and suffering of others… but I don't let it trap me. I know it has something to teach me – and them – and if I listen to my soul, I'll find a way through it.

I no longer see tunnels as endless. I no longer see life as finite. I know truth is often stranger than fiction, but that the naked truth is the only one worth having, and yeah, it will ultimately set you free. I don't measure life or happiness or pain any more in terms of before I met Charlie or after I met Charlie or anyone else. Too many times I've tried to tell myself it's the end or it's the beginning, or this happened before or this will never happen again. It just doesn't work that way. There are cycles and cycles within cycles, and most of us can't tell where we're going next – or even where we were before. So, I'm learning to go with the flow, roll with the punches, turn those walls into waves and surf them!

So… let it go… all those fragments of dreams, like trapped autumn leaves, withered but clinging, let 'em go – sweep it clean and be glad that we have the chance to start afresh each moment. For somebody like me, who always turned to a book to find the answer, I had to climb out of my head, stop flicking through the dictionary, chuck it away and allow myself to feel. All I wanna do now is throw open the window, stick my head out – stick myself out and drown in the rain. Being close to nature, being part of the raw, pulsating downpour is all I want. It is freedom, it is immersion, it's physical and soulful at the same time. I didn't have to think so hard. I didn't have to make it make sense. I didn't have to do anything but be washed clean again. Let it rain! Let it go. Let it in. Let it out. Let it be. Be love.

I still believe love makes the world go round, but you know, there are many, many ways to ride that carousel.

(It's never going to end it's never going to end it's never going to end.)

So listen, if you have a love like this, if you've known the light that never goes out – honour it, celebrate it, let it shine! Some days the light may burn more dimly than others, some days the flames may threaten to consume you; other days it burns with a steady, beautiful flame to warm your world with a cosy glow even on the rainiest, darkest day or longest, loneliest night.

I believe once this torch is lit, it will never go out, so you have to decide how you're going to carry it. You can carry it as a beacon or a burden. I carried it as both, but now I choose the beacon every time. I'll carry on carrying that beacon. Now I understand it's not about holding on to the person who ignited it, for it keeps illuminating the cavern of my soul with or without the man who lit that spark. I thank him for striking that first match. How brightly it burned! And first of all, I tried to cling to it, hold it in my hand way too tightly, thinking something this beautiful couldn't be allowed to fade away. Holding on will do nothing but damage the skin of your soul for this flame just *is*, and nobody owns it or controls it.

There is no turning back once the dance begins. Now I know both how big and how small I am – how big and how small we all are. We all *are* – we all are one whether we try to fool ourselves with partitions, chains, borders, geographical distance or belief systems. None of it diminishes the flame of true love. The time to hesitate is over. There is – I've seen it – a certain kind of light that never goes out. You're not dreaming.